ROCK AND MINE]
COLLECTING IN

CW00420841

ROCK AND MINERAL COLLECTING IN BRITAIN

PETER R. RODGERS

FABER & FABER   LONDON & BOSTON

First published in 1979
by Faber and Faber Limited
3 Queen Square London WC1
Printed in Great Britain by
BAS Printers Limited,
Over Wallop, Hampshire

© *Peter R. Rodgers 1979*

Conditions of Sale

British Library Cataloguing in Publication Data

Rodgers, Peter Rowland
    Rock and mineral collecting in Britain.
    1. Mineralogy—Collectors and collecting—Great Britain
    I. Title
    553'.0941   QE381.G7

    ISBN 0-571-10972-1
    ISBN 0-571-11266-8 Pbk

To Jennifer and Lucy, who have
suffered throughout in silence

CONTENTS

ACKNOWLEDGEMENTS

I would like to thank all the people who have helped in the preparation of this book. I am particularly indebted to the following: Mrs E. Barrett; Dr R. S. W. Braithwaite; Mr W. L. Browne; Mr J. Buys; Mr and Mrs P. Harrison; Mr R. Holmes; Mr and Mrs I. Mathews; Mr. P. Marroney; Mr McGillivray, Kildonan; Mr and Mrs J. Opie; Mr D. Rhodes; Mr T. H. Riley, Keeper in Natural History, Sheffield City Museums; Mr C. Rogers. Photographs Nos. 4, 17 and 18 are by courtesy of the Institute of Geological Sciences. The excellent photographs of mineral and rock specimens are the work of Ken Phillip of Sheffield. All the specimens illustrated form part of the author's collection and the photographs of localities are by the author. The simplified geological maps are based on the work of H.M. Geological Survey.

Finally, I would like to thank my wife, Jennifer, and all the members of my family who have helped to make this book possible.

PLATES

PREFACE

Collecting minerals, gemstones and rock specimens is one of the fastest growing hobbies in Britain. Today when the motor car has brought increased mobility to many people, it is inevitable that we should become more aware of our surroundings, more aware of our earth; and that this, in turn, should lead to a greater desire to understand it and the processes which have shaped it down the years.

The collecting fever is a characteristic feature of human nature, and like the magpie we are prone to collect and hoard. Little excuse is needed; the fact that many minerals occur in beautiful crystal forms and in a full spectrum of colours, is in itself an excellent reason for collecting them. But there is more to it than that.

Minerals are the product of the earth's formative years; the years when the earth was being shaped, years long before the advent of man. Minerals and rocks are antiques on a grand scale. We may have the pleasure of collecting them but our ownership is a transitory thing; unlike the earth we are custodians, nothing more.

Collecting specimens is not difficult and, providing the collector is aware of the difficulties and possible dangers involved, it can be one of the most rewarding of hobbies. We are indeed fortunate that Britain has so varied a geology, and that this has created a wide range of minerals and gemstones. From the sapphires of Mull to the agates of Fife, from the turquoise of Cornwall to the 'Blue John' of Derbyshire, Britain is a treasure chest full of wonderful things; so why not lift the lid and take a look inside?

CHAPTER ONE

INTRODUCING ROCKS, MINERALS AND GEMSTONES

Scenically, the British Isles constitute one of the most fascinating areas of the globe. We have plains, mountains, hills and valleys all within a very small area.

To the geologist, amateur or professional, Britain is a marvellous hunting ground. Rocks of most varieties occur somewhere within our shores and many minerals are represented in one form or another.

Scotland offers the rock or mineral collector the greatest variety. And when one considers that the Scottish Highlands are but the shattered geological remnants of a once mighty mountain chain, mightier even than the Alps or the Himalayas, it must be acknowledged that the earth's geological processes have been at their most active in what is now the British Isles.

England also has its interesting areas. Cornwall with its barren moorland scenery has yielded a wide range of mineralogical delights, as well as providing eighteenth- and nineteenth-century Britain with much valuable mineral ore. The same is true of Derbyshire and the Lake District.

It would be wrong to miss out reference to Wales and Ireland. The former is, of course, renowned for its gold mines and, like Scotland, has some of the oldest geological formations in Britain; while Northern Ireland has the great tourist attraction of the Giant's Causeway. This perfect example of a volcanic rock formation is less than 65 million years old and is a mere upstart when one considers that the earth's Odyssey started over 4,500 million years ago.

The earth started life as a glowing ball of gas, vastly different from what it is today. For millions of years the gas cooled, until eventually it became semi-liquid; not liquid like the sea, but molten rock. The earth's first rocks were formed on the surface of this slowly cooling liquid. The remains of these rocks cannot be found today.

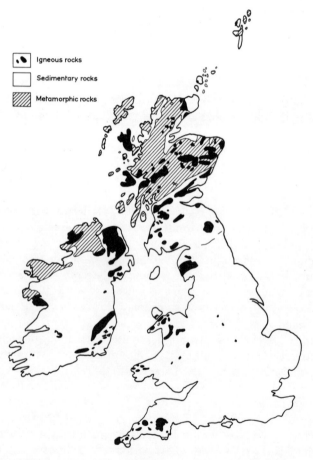

Igneous rocks

Sedimentary rocks

Metamorphic rocks

Fig. 1 A simplified geological map of the British Isles.

The evolutionary path which led to man started some 3,000 million years ago, and has created and discarded many different life forms; but man is the first of the earth's creatures capable of deciding his own future, and for the first time the hands of nature may be tied.

The surface of the earth we know today has been created by the erosion cycle, with a little recent interference by man, who would have been unable to develop a civilization had the earth not prepared certain substances for his consumption. And it is these, the earth's economic minerals, upon which man so heavily depends.

Rocks, minerals and gemstones

Rocks are the major building units of the earth. The ground beneath our feet is composed almost entirely of rocks, although there are many different varieties and several different methods by which they may have been formed.

1. Granite from the Shap Granite Quarry in Cumbria. The three constituent minerals are easily discerned. They are feldspar, in large rectangular crystals, quartz, which is white, and the black mica.

In fact, rocks are composed of minerals; granite for example is made up of three minerals, quartz, feldspar and mica; while limestone is essentially the mineral calcite, plus a variety of impurities. The constituent minerals of any rock can vary enormously in concentration, each variation producing a slightly different rock.

Minerals, on the other hand, are found only very rarely in an uncombined form. When they are found, it is usually as a fracture or cavity filling in rocks.

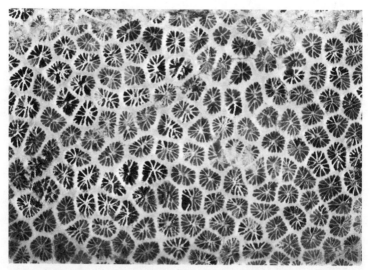

2. Limestone is often composed of fossils. The specimen illustrated is a coral limestone from Helmsdale, Sutherland.

The earth's geological processes create faults, flaws and cavities in rocks, and it is here that minerals are to be found. The formation of minerals in these situations is usually by deposition from mineral-rich liquids and gases, which emanate from within the earth.

A mineral is defined as an element, or a chemical compound, which occurs naturally within the earth's crust. The earth has ninety-two naturally occurring elements, most of which combine chemically with one another to produce minerals.

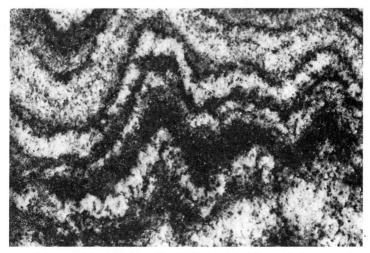

*3. Metamorphic rocks may often be distinguished due to their contorted
structure. This specimen is Lewisian Gneiss which is the oldest rock in the
British Isles.*

Take water as an example. Water is a chemical compound
composed of hydrogen and oxygen and is one of the earth's
most abundant minerals. The mineral quartz is a compound
composed of silicon and oxygen. Calcite is calcium carbonate, a
mineral made up of the elements calcium, carbon and oxygen.
Several elements such as gold, silver, copper and sulphur can
occur in the earth's crust in an uncombined state and are
therefore minerals. Most elements, however, combine so
readily with each other that they are never able to exist alone in
nature.

Economic minerals have been exploited by man for several
thousand years. The need for minerals containing metals such as
tin, lead, iron, zinc and copper has grown alongside man's
civilization. In less than 3,000 years, man has almost consumed
the materials which the earth took over 4,500 million years to
prepare.

Britain is a poor country from the point of view of mineral
wealth; and although ores of tin, zinc, copper, lead and iron
have been mined here since before Roman times, little mining
activity remains.

Rocks are plentiful. Economic minerals are, in comparison, scarce. And inevitably gemstones are very rare.

Gemstones are minerals which are either very attractive in their natural form, or become attractive when they have been subjected to the cutting and polishing skills of a lapidary.

In the past, two major categories of gemstones have been recognized, these being precious and semi-precious stones, rarity being the distinguishing factor. Emerald, sapphire, ruby and diamond are considered to be precious stones.

The term semi-precious covers a wide range of stones. Topaz, tourmaline, epidote, zircon, beryl and garnet all fall into this category, but to these one can add the quartz gemstones; amethyst, smoky quartz, citrine, morion, chalcedony, agate, onyx and even jasper. The latter is, at least as far as Britain is concerned, a most abundant gemstone.

Another factor which decides the value of a stone as a gem is its hardness. To be of real value, a polished stone in a piece of jewellery has to be immune from being scratched by the everyday objects with which it may come into contact.

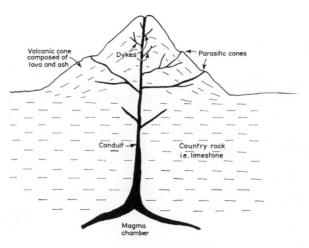

Fig. 2 Diagram of a volcano.

The hardness of minerals and gemstones is given by Mohs' Scale of Hardness, which covers ten points. Talc at 1 is the softest mineral while diamond at 10 is the hardest. Hardened steel only rates at 6.5 on this scale and consequently as a rough guide, minerals with hardness above 6.5 are most suitable for jewellery purposes.

In the chapters that follow in this book we shall learn how Britain's rocks were formed, when they were formed, and what minerals they contain.

We shall journey back 600 million years into the earth's history to see just what events have shaped our land. Unfortunately, the rock pages of Britain's history become extremely dog-eared and confusing when one endeavours to trace events which took place over 600 million years ago and as a result we will rarely step back beyond this barrier.

In the next chapters, repeated reference has had to be made to the Geological Time Scale which was created by geologists as an aid to dating rocks and to formulating the earth's history.

It is also useful to remember the origin of the names of the periods, as these are particularly relevant to Britain.

THE GEOLOGICAL TIME SCALE MILLIONS OF YEARS AGO	PERIODS
2	Quaternary
65	Tertiary
140	Cretaceous
195	Jurassic
230	Triassic
280	Permian
345	Carboniferous
395	Devonian
435	Silurian
500	Ordovician
570	Cambrian
4,600	Precambrian

CAMBRIAN comes from Cambria, the Latin name for Wales, where these rocks were first examined. ORDOVICIAN takes its name from an ancient Celtic tribe called the Ordovices, that once lived in Wales. SILURIAN also takes its name from an ancient Welsh tribe, the Silures. DEVONIAN comes from the county of Devon where these rocks were first examined. It has also been called the OLD RED SANDSTONE PERIOD because red sandstone was the characteristic rock being formed on land at the time. CARBONIFEROUS comes from the coal which was formed towards the end of the period. PERMIAN is named after the province of Perm in Russia. TRIASSIC takes its name from the Greek 'trias' which means three. There are three distinct divisions in the Triassic rocks. JURASSIC comes from the Jura Mountains between France and Switzerland. CRETACEOUS comes from the Latin word creta meaning chalk. This was the characteristic rock formed at the time. TERTIARY takes its name from an outdated rock classification. It is divided into five epochs, these being the Palaeocene, the Eocene, the Oligocene, the Miocene and the Pliocene in order of descending age. Finally we have the QUATERNARY in which we are still living today. This period also takes its name from an outdated rock classification.

The pages that lie ahead are full of strange and violent events and the terms above will help you, as you skirt the fringe of a volcano or dodge out of the path of a charging dinosaur. But in the end, when you have turned over the last page and gone into the countryside in search of rock and mineral specimens, you may recall the events described here, and think just how lucky you are to live in Britain today.

CHAPTER TWO

ROCKS AND MINERALS FROM WITHIN THE EARTH

Today Britain is a land at peace. Green meadows, woods, moorland and mountains are plentiful, and you can walk them in perfect safety, secure in the knowledge that down below the earth is still. Whichever part of our country you choose to roam, you will not stumble upon a volcano in eruption, nor be stopped in your tracks by the sudden devastation and destruction of an earthquake. Only very occasionally will a slight earth tremor take place which can remind us that once, millions of years ago, Britain was a totally different place; a place where volcanoes were numerous and earthquakes a frequent event.

Britain therefore has not always been as peaceful as it is today and in fact there has been a long history of terrestrial violence, which has transformed the landscape many times. Not once, but on several occasions, huge masses of rock have been thrust high into the sky forming great mountain chains, and on each occasion huge quantities of molten rock have been spewed over the countryside from the numerous volcanic eruptions which have accompanied such events. Earthquakes too, have shattered the structural rocks on countless occasions in the past, and each has left its own scar upon the British scene.

Igneous rocks

In this chapter our prime concern is with igneous rocks, and it is to these now that we must turn. 'Igneous' is taken from the

Latin 'ignis' (fire), and immediately the nature of igneous rocks becomes apparent. In fact, igneous rocks come from deep within the earth, rising through fissures in the rocks of the earth's crust, towards the surface. If molten rock, or magma as geologists call it, reaches the surface of the earth, a volcano is born.

Magma which is poured out upon the surface of the earth cools very rapidly in contact with the atmosphere; but not all magma reaches the surface. It is not unusual for it to eat its way into the earth's crust and yet fail to reach the surface. When this happens the molten rock cools very slowly, for it is surrounded by other rocks which prevent rapid cooling. The result is that the rapidly cooled volcanic rocks are different in texture and appearance from the rocks which have cooled within the earth, although the character of the original magma may well have been identical. In order to differentiate between these different types of rock, the volcanic rocks are termed extrusive, while the slowly cooled rocks are called intrusive. Basalt and andesite are typical of the former, while granite and gabbro exemplify the latter. Of course the molten magma which rises from within the earth may vary quite considerably in composition and this in turn can create different types of igneous rocks. Even the character of a volcano is greatly affected by the composition of the magma.

To find the origin of most of Britain's igneous rocks we shall have to turn back the geological clock, and look at events taking shape in Britain almost 500 million years ago, when the Ordovician Period of geological history was in full swing.

Our attention is first drawn to the west, to Wales. Most of Britain was underwater, but there were clouds of steam and black smoke to be seen in the distance. At this time great pressures were being exerted upon the earth's crust forcing huge areas of rock together, and volcanoes were active, belching out molten lava. Most of the volcanic activity took place underwater, and has resulted in the large masses of pillow lava which exist in North Wales. The marine nature of the vulcanism has resulted in considerable intermixing of volcanic and sedimentary rocks in this area. Volcanoes were also active at this time around the Lake District, and this is substantiated by the presence of the Borrowdale Volcanics, near Keswick.

Time marched on from the Ordovician to the Silurian Period, but although the earth movements continued, the volcanic activity decreased dramatically.

However, volcanic rocks of Silurian Age can be found in the Mendip Hills in Somerset. The Silurian was one of the briefest geological periods, but it had considerable effect upon the scenery. All the movements of the earth's crust since the Ordovician Period had been creating a new mountain chain, and the work was coming to fruition.

4. *An artist's impression of the Lake District (Eden Valley) during Ordovician times. Volcanoes are visible on the horizon, the lavas from which today form the Borrowdale Volcanics. This photograph is reproduced by courtesy of the Director of the Institute of Geological Sciences. NERC copyright.*

As the pressure on the rocks mounted, so more and more disturbances began to take place. Volcanoes blossomed forth in all their violent glory, clouds of dust and ash were blown high into the sky, and slowly but inexorably the tortured rocks began to rise. The folding was most severe in the north, in Scotland, and it was here that the volcanoes were at their most violent, but by that time the Devonian or Old Red Sandstone Period of geological history had dawned.

The Caledonian Mountains, as they have since been called, were thrust high into the Devonian skies, and have been likened to the Himalayas in their enormity. They stretched from Northern Ireland, through Scotland and across the North Sea to Norway. They certainly reached many thousands of feet in height, despite the forces of erosion taking considerable toll.

Uplift continued throughout the early Devonian Period and great quantities of volcanic rocks were formed, while large masses of granite were intruded into the base of the mountains. The remains of these now elderly lavas are quite extensive in the north of the country. The Ochil and Sidlaw Hills of Perthshire, the North Fife Hills and the Pentland Hills south of Edinburgh, all owe their origin to those far-off days. The same volcanic rocks outcrop on the coast of Ayrshire, but not in any great quantity. In Northumbria, the Cheviot Hills contain over twenty square miles of lava, which today forms the basis of the Northumberland National Park.

As the Devonian Period drew to a close the Caledonian Mountain building activity was almost over. There had inevitably been long periods of erosion or denudation, and the Caledonian Mountains of Wales and England had been well and truly flattened. Not so the mountains of Scotland, for these, together with the Scandinavian Continent, were to remain on the scene for a good many million years to come. The eventual erosion of the Caledonian Mountains was, of course, still to reveal the large granite intrusions which were hidden under many thousands of tons of rock. It is only today, when erosion has almost completed its work, that we can look upon the granite of the Grampian Mountains and say, with reasonable certainty, that these rocks were formed when the Caledonian Mountains were being created, so very long ago.

The dawn of the Carboniferous Period came, and then again volcanoes were active, extruding their molten lava over the landscape. Probably the most severely affected area was the Midland Valley of Scotland where tremendous quantities of magma were poured forth. Most of England was quiet at this time, but lava flows were being created in what is now Derbyshire's Peak District. Volcanic activity was intermittent, especially in Scotland throughout the entire period, but was becoming increasingly prevalent as the Carboniferous neared its close. It is generally considered that the Carboniferous climate had been warm and wet, but before long there would be desert conditions in Britain, for the earth was on the move again.

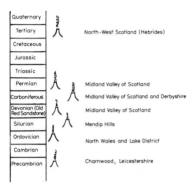

Quaternary		
Tertiary		North-West Scotland (Hebrides)
Cretaceous		
Jurassic		
Triassic		
Permian		Midland Valley of Scotland
Carboniferous		Midland Valley of Scotland and Derbyshire
Devonian (Old Red Sandstone)		Midland Valley of Scotland
Silurian		Mendip Hills
Ordovician		North Wales and Lake District
Cambrian		
Precambrian		Charnwood, Leicestershire

Fig. 3   The Geological Time Scale with relation to the main periods of volcanic activity.

The Hercynian mountain-building phase, or orogeny as it may be called, began in the dying days of the Carboniferous, and persisted through much of the Permian. As one would expect, volcanoes formed part of the process. Volcanic rocks of the Permian Age are sparse in Britain today, but they can still be found interbedded with other rocks in the county of Ayrshire. Many of the volcanic necks of Eastern Fife may also belong to this period of vulcanism. It was at this time that large masses of igneous rocks were formed by the intrusion of molten magma, into what the geologists call the Cornubrian Mountains. The subsequent erosion of these mountains has revealed the granite which today forms the attractive moorland scenery of Devon and Cornwall.

Geologists have now proved that the granite of Dartmoor, Bodmin Moor, St Austell, Carnmenellis, Land's End and even the Scilly Isles is all linked together underground. They are all part of one great batholith. ('Batholith' is the term used to describe the largest of igneous intrusions, which may cover thousands of square miles.) Apart from Cornwall and Devon, the Cairngorm Mountains of Scotland and the Mourne

Mountains of Ireland are examples of giant batholiths that have been revealed by erosion. Laccoliths are smaller intrusions which are mushroom-shaped and often give rise to a dome-shaped hill, Corndon Hill in Shropshire being a classic example.

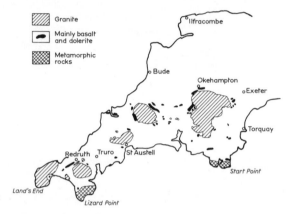

Fig. 4 A map showing the igneous rocks in Cornwall.

The Hercynian Orogeny resulted in the uplifting of the Mercian Highlands, the Pennine area and Lake District, but the Permian Period was generally a time of rapid erosion. Desert conditions continued in Britain during the Triassic Period and although the rocks which formed the British Isles were uplifted during the subsequent Jurassic and Cretaceous Periods, there was a cessation of volcanic and other igneous activity. In fact from the Permian Period it would be over 200 million years before a volcano erupted again in Britain.

The Tertiary Period began about 60 million years ago and, at least as far as Britain is concerned, it came in to the roar of numerous volcanoes. The Alpine Orogeny was in full swing at this time but the major events which affected Britain occurred many millions of years after the vulcanism had died down. Compared with the effect of the Caledonian and the Hercynian Orogenies, the Alpine folding had little effect on Britain, but was responsible for the geography of the Wealden area and much of Southern England.

The new volcanoes were very extensive off the western

seaboard of Scotland, and huge lava flows resulted. Today they form the beautiful scenery of the Hebridean Islands of Mull, Skye and the mainland at Ardnamurchan. There were many volcanoes giving off great quantities of basaltic lava, and today the remains of several volcanoes are known in the Hebrides. This volcanic activity was not confined to Scotland, but covered much of the area between Scotland, Ireland and Iceland. The Giant's Causeway and surrounding area of Antrim in Ireland is composed of the same volcanic rocks, and the volcanoes which still exist on Iceland today are an extension of this period of vulcanism. It is considered that the mineral veins which exist in the limestones of the Lake District were formed at this time.

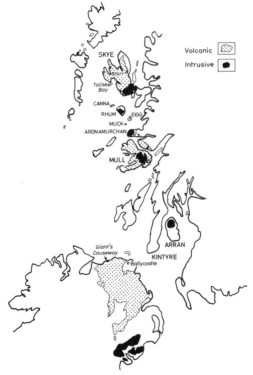

Fig. 5 The volcanic centres of Tertiary Age and the distribution of the volcanic rocks they produced.

Intrusive igneous rocks were formed and today these are revealed in the Mourne Mountains of Ireland, the Cuillins of Skye and around Goatfell on the Isle of Arran. Further igneous activity, in the form of sills and dykes, also took place and was far-reaching in its extent. The Cleveland Dyke in North Yorkshire is a result of the disturbances which took place in the Tertiary Period.

A dyke is a vertical sheet of igneous rock, which usually has ascended through a vertical fault or fissure in the existing rocks, and cuts across the bedding planes. However, should the magma find a less difficult path along a bedding plane then a sill is formed. Technically a sill runs parallel to the bedding planes, while a dyke cuts across them.

The best known example of a sill in Britain is the famous Whin Sill, which traverses the north of England through Northumberland and Durham. This sill is of Carboniferous Age, but examples of sills of Tertiary Age are quite common in the west of Scotland. Dykes often occur in great numbers, and such concentrations are called swarms. These igneous rock forms are to be expected wherever volcanoes or mountain-building forces have been at work.

The igneous rocks of the Hebrides have been extensively eroded during the last 55 million years and are much less abundant than when they were originally created.

As far as Britain is concerned there has been no volcanic activity since the Tertiary, but the country has had a long history of vulcanism, and there can be little doubt that at some future date, it will return.

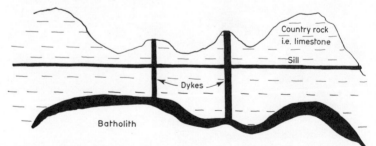

Fig. 6 A diagram showing sills and dykes in relation to a batholith, and the sedimentary rocks which surround them.

Formation of minerals from within the earth

Whenever magma rises up into the earth's crust there is a high possibility that mineral deposits will be formed. Magma contains a mixture of minerals at a high temperature, but as the temperature falls, the different minerals begin to separate out, the rock-forming minerals solidifying first.

The residual, volatile-rich fluids derived from cooling magmas, especially granites, rise upwards along cracks and fissures towards the earth's surface, cooling to form mineral veins. When magma is surrounded by cold rocks it will cool fairly rapidly, and with fall in temperature more minerals will be deposited successively, one upon another, in order of their decreasing melting points. This is how mineral veins are built up.

If a small amount of residue from cooling magma becomes highly charged with water at low pressures it may solidify to produce crystals of tourmaline, topaz, mica and felspar, this being a pegmatite formation.

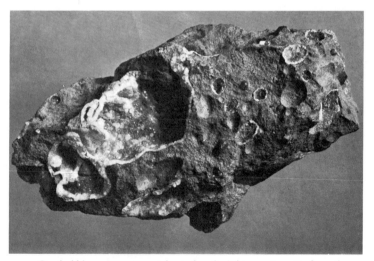

5. *Gas bubble cavities or vesicles in basalt. This specimen is from the Tertiary Lavas at Talisker Bay, Isle of Skye. The vesicles are lined with crystals of analcite and some small fibres of natrolite, both zeolite minerals. Size 112 × 80 mm.*

As the magma cools still further more minerals separate out, leaving a more liquid magma which contains a greater proportion of gas. Of the gases, steam is present in great quantities and this dissolves minerals such as quartz or calcite out of existing rocks and redeposits them in fissures in the surrounding rock. This is called hydrothermal activity.

Gas cavities in lava

Gases such as sulphur dioxide, carbon dioxide, chlorine and water vapour are liberated in great quantities from cooling magma, in which they are present in the form of bubbles.

In the case of lava flows, many of the gas bubbles are trapped within the lava as it solidifies. When the lava has become rock the gases diffuse out leaving a bubble shape behind. The bubble cavities are called vesicles, and often become filled with such materials as quartz, agate, chalcedony and calcite, which are deposited by hydrothermal action.

Pegmatites

The name pegmatite comes from the Greek 'pegma', meaning coarse or thick, and is used to describe a rather unusual mineral occurrence.

A pegmatite is a rock, usually of granitic composition, which is made up of extremely large crystals. The most common minerals are quartz, feldspar and mica, but rarer minerals such as topaz, tourmaline and cairngorm (smoky quartz) may also occur. It is not unusual for a rock of this type to have hollow areas with fine, well-developed crystals protruding inwards from each rock face.

A pegmatite is usually present as a dyke or sheet, but the large crystals it contains also help you to identify it. Although not to be expected in Britain, it is known for single crystals in some pegmatites to weigh many tons and be hundreds of feet in length.

CHAPTER THREE

MINERALS IN BRITAIN'S IGNEOUS ROCKS

In Britain, the greatest variety of igneous rocks is to be found in Scotland, and it is here that our search must begin.

Scotland

Erosion has taken great toll of Scotland's igneous rocks down the years but despite this, there are many areas for the collector to examine.

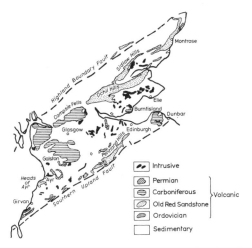

Fig. 7 The distribution of igneous rocks in the Midland Valley of Scotland.

Volcanic rocks are chiefly to be found in the Midland Valley, which contains the rivers Forth and Clyde, and is bounded by the Highland Boundary Fault in the north, and the Southern Uplands Fault in the south. It is the remains of a rift valley which subsided at the end of the Carboniferous Period of geological history, 250 million years ago.

The lavas here, which are of Devonian and Carboniferous Ages, are abundant and contain a variety of interesting minerals.

The Devonian lavas, which are basalts and andesites, are famous for their association with one particular semi-precious stone called agate. Agate has been formed in the gas cavities (vesicles) in the lavas, and is present in some considerable abundance. However, amethyst, smoky quartz, rock crystal and calcite also occur in the same situation. Agate is often strongly banded, attractively coloured, and is probably the most popular of Britain's gemstones.

6. *Agates from the Old Red Sandstone lavas of Scotland's Midland Valley. Top left: onyx island agate from Dunure, Ayrshire; top centre: onyx/agate from Dunure; top right: fortification agate from Usan, Angus; bottom left: fortification agate from Usan, Angus; bottom centre: onyx agate from Usan, Angus; bottom right: flame agate from Balmeadowside, Fife. Size (top centre) 60 × 60 mm.*

No two agates are ever identical, but they may quite frequently have similar patterns. This fact has made it possible to categorize agates into certain varieties. There is fortification agate, which resembles the aerial view of a castle; and eye agate, which, not surprisingly, resembles the human eye; while onyx is straight parallel bands of agate. However, probably the most attractive are landscape agates which resemble country or coastal scenes. Another variety, moss agate, contains small green mineral inclusions, which create a moss-like pattern in the stone. The true beauty of an agate can only be appreciated when it has been cut and polished.

Agates occur at many localities throughout the Old Red Sandstone lavas. Montrose, in the north-east of the Midland Valley, is based on the agate-bearing volcanic rocks, and good sites nearby include the beach at Ferryden and the rocks by Scurdie Ness Lighthouse. Usan, six miles to the south, is also a good place to search. Agates also turn up in the shingle of Lunan Bay, together with jasper and occasionally hematite. Further south in the Sidlaw Hills of Perthshire, agates can be found with amethyst on Kings Seat (376 m) and some of the most beautiful agates in Britain occur at Agate Knowe on the nearby farmland of Ballindean. Kinnoul Hill and Pole Hill, near the city of Perth, are also reasonable localities. The Ochil Hills of Perthshire contain several good agate sites including the farmland of Glen Farg, and around Path of Condie.

Probably the most productive agate area in Britain is the North Fife Hills. The hills are composed of andesite, of Old Red Sandstone Age, and are really an extension of the Ochil Hills. Normans Law (300 m), the highest of the North Fife Hills, is a good place to start your search, but all the farmland in the area will yield specimens not only of agate, but also of amethyst, cairngorm, rock crystal and occasionally opal. Wad, otherwise known as manganese dioxide, also occurs on Normans Law.

Agate, along with the orange carnelian and the grey common chalcedony, occurs as pebbles on beaches along the south bank of the Firth of Tay, and specimens may be found around Carlops in the Pentland Hills, south of Edinburgh. Dunure on the west coast, south of the city of Ayr, is a good site for agate and amethyst, but excellent specimens of agates have been found in the Burn Anne, south-east of Galston.

The Carboniferous lavas are strangely different from those of Old Red Sandstone Age. In the first place the lava is essentially basalt and not andesite, and secondly, while minerals are reasonably common in the gas cavities, agates are exceedingly scarce.

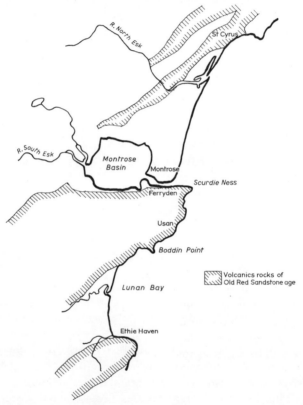

Fig. 8 A map showing the agate-bearing volcanic rocks around Montrose.

The Renfrewshire uplands form what is probably the largest area of Carboniferous basalt, but basalt also occurs near Haddington in East Lothian and on the Campsie and Kilpatrick Hills north of Glasgow. Zeolites are the most abundant find in these lavas and the area is famous for excellent specimens. Natrolite and prehnite can be found at Bishopstown and on Hartfield Moss in the county of Renfrewshire, the former site being famous for the cadmium mineral greenockite. Natrolite, together with amethyst, is a possible find on the Campsie Fells, while chalcedony and calcite may occur at all the basalt localities.

The Carboniferous volcanic rocks of Fife also contain a variety of minerals including agate, chalcedony and rock crystal in the Lomond Hills, and jasper and natrolite in the basalt at Burntisland. The lavas can also be found at Blackford Hill Quarry in Edinburgh, where amethyst and agate, the latter in a vein form, occur. Craiglockhart Quarry and Corstorphine Hill are localities for amethyst.

Zeolites are the main prize in the Carboniferous lavas but prehnite, which is an associate mineral, can also be located.

Volcanic necks of Carboniferous Age are numerous in the Midland Valley and have a characteristic oval outline. Being harder than the sedimentary rocks which surround them, they usually stand out as small hills, which appear out of character with their surroundings. Arthur's Seat at Edinburgh, and Binn Hill at Burntisland are excellent examples of volcanic necks. Red pyrope garnets occur in a similar situation at Elie Ness, in the south of Fife, where zircon has also been reported.

In the south of Scotland, Old Red Sandstone lavas outcrop on the Scottish side of the Cheviot Hills, and agates are known to occur in these lavas near Jedburgh.

The Lorne Plateau around Oban, in Argyll, is also composed of Old Red Sandstone lavas but these are essentially devoid of minerals. However, agates occur on the volcanic crest of Ben Nevis, a few miles away to the north.

Oban is the gateway to the Hebridean islands of Mull and Iona, although the Trishnish Islands and Staffa are all close by. Basalt, this time of Tertiary Age, dominates Mull, and in fact the core of one of the Tertiary volcanoes is exposed in the south of the Island. Staffa is of course famous for its columnar basalt, which is extremely picturesque and surrounds Fingal's Cave. Columnar basalt is created as the volcanic rock cools. In fact it shrinks and splits into the vertical columns which are characteristic of the site mentioned. The Giant's Causeway in Northern Ireland is another such site.

Again, zeolites are the most common minerals in the basalts of Mull and can be expected at almost every rock exposure.

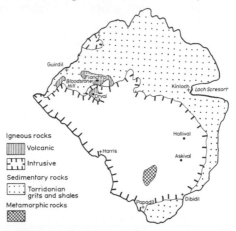

Fig. 9 A geological map of the Isle of Rhum. Geologists believe the island is the remains of a volcano.

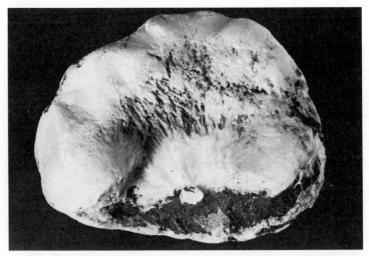

7. Natrolite is common in cavities in volcanic rocks of Carboniferous and Tertiary Ages. The specimen illustrated is from Scoor on the Isle of Mull. Size 80 × 40 mm.

Natrolite is probably the most common, with analcite a close second. Beaches to the south-east of Scoor, in the Ross of Mull, offer not only prehnite but also carnelian, agate, chalcedony, rock crystal and amethyst. Agate crops up again in rocks on the shore at Scobul on the north bank of Loch Scridain.

The Isle of Rhum, which is the largest of the 'Small Isles', is believed by geologists to be the remains of one of the volcanoes of the Tertiary Period. Agate occurs with bloodstone on the beach at Guirdil Bay, and both can be located on the flanks of Bloodstone Hill on the west of the island. The bloodstone has been used for decorative purposes and was once quarried near Bloodstone Hill. Today the island belongs to the Nature Conservancy and minerals are only to be collected when a permit has been obtained from the Chief Warden.

8. The tall basalt pinnacle of the 'Old Man of Storr' is a classic locality for mineral collectors on the Isle of Skye. Minerals to be found here include analcite, natrolite and stilbite.

Further north, the basalt of the Isle of Skye contains a wealth of zeolites, fine examples of which are common at Talisker Bay on the west of the island, where jasper opal also occurs; and at Storr in the east near Portree. The unusual basalt pinnacles which form the 'Old Man of Storr and his family' make an interesting land mark, and the screes which lie around their shoulders are very productive of zeolite mineral specimens including stilbite. Onyx has been reported at Storr, but I have been unable to confirm this, although I have found pale blue chalcedony. Agate is known near Dunvegan and I have found sardonyx and carnelian, by Colbost on Loch Dunvegan.

Granite and gabbro form the Tertiary intrusive rocks of Skye and occur around Sligachan. The Red Hills are composed of granite which may yield cairngorm; and the Cuillins which are made up of gabbro occasionally give up specimens of spinel, augite and prehnite.

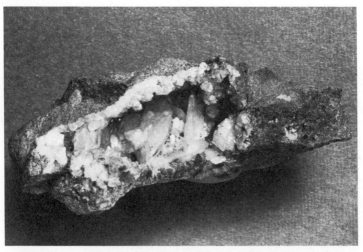

9. *Stilbite crystals lining a gas cavity in basalt. This specimen is from Storr on the Isle of Skye. Size 60 × 25 mm.*

Intrusive igneous rocks occur throughout the Highlands and commonly contain many minerals. The much sought after pegmatites are probably at their most common in the north, and one frequently hears reference to the many beautiful and exotic minerals they contain, but that is as may be. The geology of the Northern Highlands has yet to be fully catalogued, but granite and syenite occur in some profusion in the east. The Helmsdale granite is one of the most extensive, but syenite forms the bulk of Ben Loyal, near Tongue. Pegmatites are reputedly common, and apart from fluorite which occurs in syenite near Laird and Helmsdale, zircon, beryl, tourmaline, cairngorm and amazonite occur on the mighty Ben Loyal. Zircon also occurs on nearby Ben Hope. During the last century small diamonds were reported three miles north-east of Ben Hope, but this would appear to be an unlikely occurrence and is definitely an unsubstantiated one.

10. Ben Loyal on the north coast of Sutherland is composed of syenite, a rock related to granite. It is the home of many minerals which occur in pegmatites.

Chalcedony is attributed to Melsetta in Orkney; but we have to move northwards before we find amethyst and rock crystal, this time amongst the intrusive igneous rocks of Shetland.

It was near Helmsdale, in the Suisgill and Kildonan Burns in 1868 that gold was first discovered in the Northern Highlands of Scotland. Not unnaturally this resulted in something of a traditional gold rush. Unfortunately there was more rush than gold and all serious mining activities ceased after a year. Although set amongst igneous rock scenery the gold is alluvial.

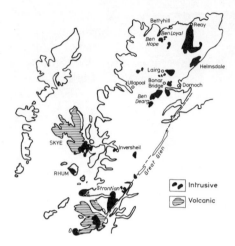

Fig. 10 The igneous rocks of the Northern Highlands of Scotland.

Thus ended Helmsdale's main claim to fame, but the burns have continually replenished themselves down the years and amateurs who go to the trouble of obtaining the necessay permits may still try their luck in the once glittering water.

Beryl, tourmaline, zircon and garnet are credited to Allt Dearg in Ross-shire, and almandine garnet occurs near Strathpeffer, in granite. Zircon also occurs in granite at the head of Allt Graad on Loch Glass.

Strontian on Loch Sunart is situated amidst a large granite mass, which contains mineral veins. Galena and zinc blende (sphalerite) were mined here from 1722 to 1822, and other minerals including calcite, baryte and strontianite also occur, the latter mineral being a carbonate of strontium.

Intrusive rocks are much more abundant south of the great glen and mineral occurrences are plentiful. The Cairngorm Mountains, which rise to a height of 1,309 m at Ben Macdhui, are carved out of granite which dates back to the Caledonian Orogeny. The Cairngorm Mountains are the home of one of Britain's most famous stones, cairngorm. This is a honey-brown variety of crystalline quartz and outside this country is called smoky quartz. Cairngorm crystals up to 23 kilograms (50 lb) in weight have been found on Cairngorm, the mountain.

11. The author panning for gold in the Suisgill Burn near Helmsdale, Sutherland. The gold is often found amongst the roots of moss and in deep cracks in the bed rock.

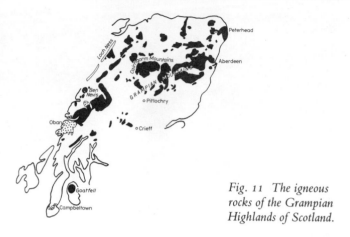

Fig. 11   The igneous rocks of the Grampian Highlands of Scotland.

Specimens can be found today, but they are scarce. Milky quartz crystals and rock crystal (colourless quartz) also occur here. Beryl, of the green variety called emerald, is found in these mountains, as is topaz, which may be blue or yellow.

12. *Specimens of rock crystal and milky quartz from the granite pegmatites of Cairngorm. Size (milky quartz) 35 × 25 mm.*

13. Rubislaw Granite Quarry was once the home of many beautiful minerals. Today the quarry, which is 148 m (485 ft) deep and is the biggest granite hole in Europe is totally inaccessible. Photograph by courtesy of Mr W. Spence.

Aberdeen, 'the granite city', is famous for one particular site known as Rubislaw Quarry, once described as the biggest hole in Europe. Here yellow beryl, with the precious multi-coloured tourmaline, and garnet have been found in the past. Unfortunately this site is no longer accessible to collectors.

Blue crystals of fluorite are known in the Peterhead granite at Murdoch Head Quarry, but the same mineral in different colours occurs quite widely throughout the intrusive rocks of the area.

Intrusive igneous rocks are common in the Midland Valley, but do not occur in large masses. They do contain minerals, but are completely overshadowed by the lavas we have already described.

Agates have been formed in a conglomerate of Old Red Sandstone Age on the Mull of Kintyre, where amethyst occurs in Carboniferous basaltic lava up Glen Wigle. Jasper-agate occurs in the same lavas on Killelan Hill, south of Campbeltown.

A large mass of granite occurs on the Isle of Arran. Goatfell (874 m), has been carved out of granite of Tertiary Age, and cairngorm occurs here together with beryl, of the variety aquamarine, and topaz. Epidote has also been reported.

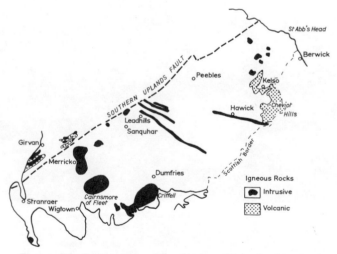

Fig. 12 The igneous rocks of the Southern Uplands of Scotland.

And so we come to the south of Scotland, the area known to geologists as the Southern Uplands. Here the main areas of intrusive rocks occur in the west; and a quick glance at the appropriate geological map shows that very large granite masses occur near Criffel, Cairnsmore of Fleet, and Merrick. Similar rocks can also be seen in the north-east near Dunbar.

Sphene has been reported in the hills near New Abbey, while tourmaline can be found on Knocknairling Hill, near New Galloway. Zircon is to be found in granite boulders in the Burn of Palnure near Cairnsmuir and in the Shaw Hill granite. Hematite has been worked in the granite of Loch Doon but also occurs in the Criffel granite of Kirkcudbright. The copper ores, including malachite and chalcopyrite, together with baryte, have been mined in the Priestlaw Granite in East Lothian.

Stibnite has been located in a small granite mass by The Knipe near New Cumnock in Ayrshire.

England and Wales

Once south of the Scottish borders igneous rocks are few and far between and for the most part they are confined to the areas which are popular with tourists; areas such as the Lake District, the Cheviot Hills and North Wales.

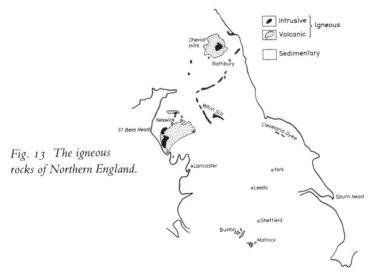

Fig. 13 The igneous rocks of Northern England.

Volcanic rocks of Old Red Sandstone Age are prolific in the Cheviot Hills where agate, chalcedony, rock crystal and amethyst are common finds, especially in the south, near Alwinton. The Cheviot Hills are the remains of a volcano, which accounts for the large area of andesitic lava. The Cheviot itself, which stands 931 m high, is granite of the same age, and milky quartz crystals, rock crystal and tourmaline are fairly common.

I have already explained the nature of sills and dykes, and these are in fact much more common than reference to them in these pages may suggest. There are however two occurrences of these igneous rock formations which are worthy of mention. The first is the Whin Sill, which is of Carboniferous Age and stretches from the east coast of Northumberland, south to Teesdale. I have found pyrites, milky quartz crystals and pale banded agate on the sill. Further south the Cleveland Dyke cuts across North Yorkshire, but regrettably does not yield mineral specimens.

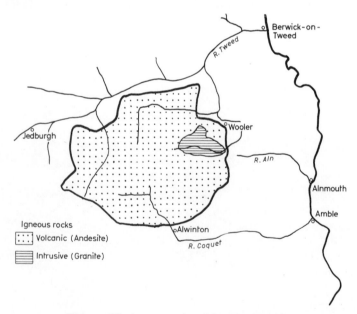

Fig. 14   The igneous rocks of the Cheviot Hills.

The Lake District dominates the scenery in the north-west of England and volcanic rocks of Ordovician Age are represented by the Borrowdale Volcanics, which lie to the south of Keswick and have created much of the beautiful lakeland scenery. Epidote, in good crystal specimens, occurs on the east of Derwentwater on Walla Crag; and at the top of Cat Gyll, agate, chalcedony, quartz and amethyst may be found, but are of comparatively little distinction. Garnets are common in the lavas at the head of Wastwater. Zircon and sphene occur in the intrusive rocks of Ennerdale while cairngorm, or smoky quartz, is well known for its occurrence on Cleator Moor.

Most collectors will have heard mention of Calbeck Fells and it is here, amongst an igneous rock complex, that a wide and interesting variety of minerals occurs. It is the famous Carrock mine which deserves attention from the collector, for here there has been a long history of mining, and on spoil heaps mineral specimens are fairly common. Scheelite, the tungsten ore, has been mined here, but citrine (yellow quartz), apatite, tourmaline, and corundum and gold are associated with this mine. The Carrock area is also the scene of other mines with their respective dumps, and copper ores which include malachite, bornite and chrysocolla are possible finds. The entire Caldbeck region is rather inaccessible and collectors should only venture forth when prepared for a long trek.

Our attention must now turn southwards to Shap Fell. The Shap granite quarry is known to yield good specimens of fluorite (fluorspar), cairngorm and rock crystal. The Shap granite is particularly attractive and at the same time unusual. It is essentially pink in colour, due to the feldspar constituent, which is present in the form of large, well-developed crystals. This stone has found much application as a building and facing stone, and examples can be seen in many parts of the country.

Derbyshire's Peak District is the next area where volcanic rocks occur, but here they are not in any great concentration. The volcanic rocks, or toadstones as they are called locally, are most common around Buxton and Matlock.

These igneous rocks have been worked for road building purposes at two quarries in the area and minerals have been found at each. Calton Hill, a now disused quarry, has yielded a wide variety of minerals including amethyst, smoky quartz, rock crystal, red jasper and olivine, the first in fine crystal specimens. Good finds are much rarer today as no new surfaces have been revealed since the quarrying ceased. North of Buxton at Waterswallow Quarry, amethyst can be found, together with agate. This is a working quarry (1975) and new rock surfaces are constantly being revealed. Of course access to private sites is only possible when permission has been obtained from the owner and the collector should never enter such sites without first obtaining this.

The volcanic rocks also outcrop in Millersdale, and agate, chalcedony and quartz occur here. Lavas outcrop in a very small area at the top of Cavedale, near Castleton, where chalcedony may be found.

In Wales, igneous rocks are mainly confined to the north where they are responsible for much of the beautiful scenery. Volcanic rocks of Ordovician Age form the bulk of Snowdonia, but these are young upstarts compared with the Precambrian intrusive rocks of Anglesey, and the rhyolitic lavas of the Lleyn Peninsula.

In Central Wales we find small areas of basalt between Llandrindod and Builth Wells, in Radnorshire; while andesites and rhyolites are prominent along the coast of Pembrokeshire between Strumble Head and Fishguard, in South Wales.

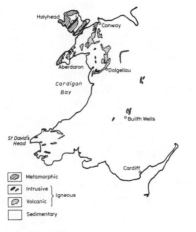

Fig. 15 Igneous and metamorphic rocks in Wales.

Minerals are scarce in these igneous rocks and nowhere could they be said to exist in abundance. Copper minerals occur around Snowdon and rock crystal is reasonably common.

Chlorite, sphene, calcite and quartz are linked to the basalt quarries near Llandrindod and poor quality agate may also be found here.

In the volcanic rocks of Pembrokeshire, minerals it seems are conspicuous by their absence, but jasper occurs in these rocks at Strumble Head, and hematite crystals can be found in quartz veins.

Diorite, an intrusive igneous rock, which is similar in appearance to granite, contains crystals of hornblende, near Hollybush, while apatite, sphene, and ilmenite join with hornblende in the same rock at Knaveston.

Precambrian volcanic rocks form the Wrekin in Shropshire, while andesitic lavas of Devonian Age occur in the Mendip Hills in Somerset. Unfortunately these rocks are only present in small amounts. Chalcedony is a common find at the latter locality.

Volcanic rocks of Precambrian Age outcrop in the Charn-wood area of Leicestershire and are accompanied by a large intrusion of syenite. However, minerals are not a feature of these old and battered rocks. They are surrounded by sedimentary rocks of Triassic Age, which have been heavily eroded over the years.

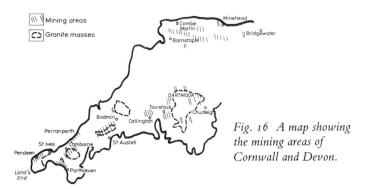

Fig. 16 A map showing the mining areas of Cornwall and Devon.

And so we come to Cornwall and Devon, and here volcanic rocks are sparse; consequently it is left to the great granite masses of the moorland areas to represent the bulk of the igneous rock family.

The granites were formed during the Hercynian earth movements and as they cooled, volatile gases were given off which included large amounts of fluorine and boron, together with sulphur dioxide, carbon dioxide and superheated steam. The gases were dissolved in fluids which entered rock crevices in the granite and surrounding rocks, giving rise to the mineral veins.

Over the years, the mineral veins of Cornwall and Devon have been worked extensively for the ores of copper, tin, iron, lead, zinc and silver; while lesser quantities of baryte, fluorspar, tungsten, nickel, uranium, cobalt, bismuth and molybdenum ores have been located.

The remains of the many old mines in the area are evidence enough of the abundance of minerals, and unfortunately it is not possible to list all the localities and the minerals that occur. Consequently I have selected the sites which provide the largest and most interesting array of minerals. In all instances, minerals can be found on the old mine dumps which surround the workings.

14. *Spoil heaps associated with the old tin mines of Cornwall contain many beautiful mineral specimens. The old engine house illustrated is at Bottalack.*

It should become obvious as you set about collecting Cornwall's minerals that the veins are often present in the surrounding country rock locally known as the Killas, and are not confined to the granite. However, in each instance the minerals can be traced back to gas emanation and hydrothermal activity, which were directly related to the granite magma.

In Cornwall, the major mining centres were around St Just and St Ives on the Land's End granite; between Penzance, Camborne, St Day, St Agnes and Newquay; and to the north of St Austell. The mining areas thin out towards Devon, but occur again to the east of Callington and on the fringes of the Dartmoor granite. Another mining area exists to the east of Barnstaple in North Devon.

The St Just mining area is possibly most famous for the uranium minerals associated with Wheal Edward, but botryoidal hematite occurs at the Botallack mine, and nearby Wheal Cock may yield apatite, amethyst, carnelian, fluorite and cassiterite.

The beach at Marazion, in Mount's Bay, has been very productive in the past, but is suffering from over-exploitation today. Citrine, carnelian, agate, amethyst and jasper have been found here in the past. Pyromorphite, the green ore of lead, can be found with dolomite crystals and galena at Penberthy Crofts; and pyrite, arsenopyrite and chalcopyrite are potential finds at Enny's Wheal Virgin in the same area, behind Marazion.

The Carn Brea Mines near Camborne yield malachite, tourmaline and amethyst, while North Roskear mine has bornite and sphalerite on its heaps. Fire opal has been recorded at Wheal Gorland near St Day.

Around St Austell the mines take on a rather different look. The old engine houses are still there but they are overshadowed by the tall white heaps of the China Clay pits. Kaolin, for this is the material being extracted, is formed by the hydrothermal alteration of the feldspar constituent of the granite. High pressure jets of water are used to strike the working face of the clay pit, bringing the clay off as a slurry. After separation, the clay is sold for use in the manufacture of paper and pottery. Specimens of amethyst, smoky quartz and black tourmaline are common throughout the china clay. In addition, turquoise can be found at Wheal Bunny with smoky quartz, and again at Gunheath Quarry and Goonvean Quarry. Beryl has been found at the Old Beam Mine and topaz at Belowda and Castle-an-Dinas; at the latter with wavellite and gold.

Near St Agnes, the Cligga Mine has yielded an impressive list of minerals including topaz, andalusite, gold, native copper, molybdenite and fluorite.

In Eastern Cornwall there are several mines and quarries which yield interesting minerals. Chalcocite, chrysocolla, chalcopyrite, malachite and azurite, which are all copper ores, occur with native copper at Wheal Phoenix; and gypsum, sphalerite, baryte, fluorite and pyrite occur at Wheal Mary Ann. Black tourmaline, otherwise known as schorl, occurs on white quartz at Roche Rock. The entire structure of the rock contains tourmaline, and it is the best example of its type in Cornwall.

If we now journey over the border into Devon we first come to the B. R. Meldon Quarry which may yield garnet, axinite, andalusite, rhodonite, opal, cairngorm and rock crystal, while the Aplite Quarry has pink and green tourmaline as well as blue beryl and cairngorm.

Baryte occurs at Bridford in the east and magnetite at Haytor. At Ramsley one can find actinolite and garnet, which further extends the range of interesting minerals to be found in the south-west.

There are a good many mines between Barnstaple and the Quantock Hills in North Devon, and the ores of iron, copper, manganese, zinc and lead have all been extracted in quantity.

At this point we must curtail our visit to Cornwall but we shall return again when we come to consider the rocks which are formed by metamorphism.

Ireland

The geology of Ireland is something of a mixture and igneous rocks are well represented.

Ordovician volcanic rocks exist near Waterford and lavas of Carboniferous Age occur near Kanturk in Cork. Granite is abundant to the south of Dublin and more can be found in the west at Galway Bay. Turning north we find more granite in the

Slieve Gamph and Ox Mountain and again in the mountains of Donegal.

The Leinster Granite, which is of Caledonian Age, contains cairngorm, and almandine garnet, while beryl and black tourmaline are known at Roundwood. Pegmatites occur here and spodumene has been found in them. Fluorite, garnet and tourmaline occur on Dalkey Island and apatite is credited to Killiney Hill.

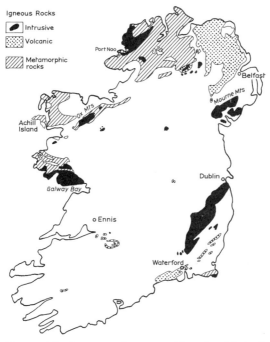

Fig. 17 The igneous and metamorphic rocks of Ireland.

Turning to the west, the granite of Galway yields sphene, garnet, galena and fluorite. The granite of Donegal contains beryl, which is grass green in colour, also rock crystal, apatite, garnet and tourmaline.

Northern Ireland has had a violent geological past, and this is testified to by the vast quantities of basalt of Tertiary Age which occur in Antrim. These are lavas contemporary with those found in the Hebrides and they commonly contain agate and chalcedony in gas cavities, together with opal, olivine and fluorite. The famous Giant's Causeway is a well known feature of the basalts.

Finally, we must turn southwards to the Mountains of Mourne which are composed of granite. The chief mineral finds here are blue beryl, fluorite, topaz, stilbite, amethyst and more commonly smoky quartz.

This brings our mineral collecting trip around Britain's igneous rocks to a close, but before we move on to rocks from beneath the sea, special reference must be made to one mineral. We have seen how quartz in its many gemstone varieties is common in igneous rocks, but this same mineral in its white or yellow massive form is abundant in veins and fissures throughout many rocks, in which form it has little appeal.

CHAPTER FOUR

FROM SEDIMENT TO STONE

If you turn to a geological map, you will immediately become aware that sedimentary rocks occur in great profusion within our shores. The east and south-east of England are composed almost entirely of these rocks, but they still occur in quantities throughout the rest of the British Isles, where they are intermingled with rocks of other varieties.

The Pennine Hills are carved out of limestone and sandstone, which are two of the most abundant sedimentary rocks. The wolds of Lincolnshire and Yorkshire, the South Downs and Dover's white cliffs are composed of chalk; the moorland of Southern Scotland is also sedimentary in origin, but there are examples galore elsewhere.

Unlike igneous rocks, which are formed when the earth is in a constructive mood, sedimentary rocks are created in exactly the opposite way, by the destruction of great mountains and continents.

Every time it rains or the sun shines, every night when there is a frost, each time a wave breaks upon the sea shore, you are seeing the forces of erosion at work. Erosion is the term used to describe the destruction of rocks by nature's forces, and over the years they have sounded the death knell of many a mountain chain. True, these forces work exceedingly slowly, but in areas where the earth's rocks are of a soft character, erosion can move ahead rapidly.

A good example of rapid erosion can be found on the Yorkshire coast, south of Flamborough Head. Erosion has

moved so rapidly here that several small but thriving villages
which existed 150 years ago have totally disappeared.

When erosion takes place the rocks on the earth's surface are
slowly worn away. The fractured and broken debris is washed
down into rivers and streams, eventually to reach the sea where
it sinks to the bottom of the ocean to lie undisturbed.

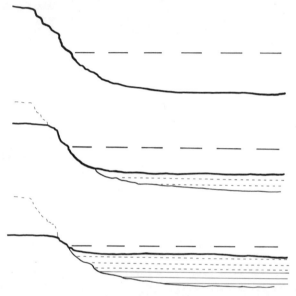

*Fig. 18 The formation of sedimentary rocks. This simplified diagram
shows how the erosion of large areas of rock leads to the deposition of
sediments which later become sedimentary rocks.*

As time passes, rock debris piles up beneath the sea. The more
debris, the greater the pressure, until eventually, either due to
weight of debris, or to some folding of the earth's crust, these
fragments are bonded together into rock. A bonding agent such
as calcite or quartz usually forms the matrix in which the debris
is held. It is only millions of years later when the rocks of the
earth's crust are being moved about, that these sedimentary
rocks are brought to the surface, to be eroded in their turn.

The character of sedimentary rocks formed from rock debris
is dependent upon the nature of the original material from

which it was eroded. If the eroded sediment came from a freshly eroded feldspar-rich rock, then feldspar will play an important role in the appearance of the new rock. The Millstone Grit, which forms so many attractive 'edges' in North Derbyshire and Yorkshire is a sedimentary rock formed by the erosion of a rock rich in feldspar.

The size of the sedimentary particles also plays an important part in deciding the nature of a particular rock. A conglomerate is composed of large pebbles which are cemented together. However, should the material be angular rather than pebble-shaped, then the resulting rock is a breccia. Particles of sand grain size form a sandstone, while slightly coarser fragments create a gritstone. A shale or clay is composed of the finest particles.

Rocks produced from sediment which has been eroded from existing rocks are called clastic sediments, but now we must consider the chemical sediments, which are formed in a totally different way.

Deep within the oceans of the earth there live great colonies of minute sea creatures—creatures which individually cannot be seen with the naked eye, but collectively have given rise to the great masses of limestone which now exist in various parts of Britain.

These small creatures secrete lime out of sea water to form the hard shell in which they live, and it is this hard shell, or skeleton, which later forms the limestone rock. In fact, rocks of this type are formed of fossils. Chalk is a pure form of limestone and may be composed in part of the remains of the sea creature, foraminifera; but there are other creatures, some of which lived in colonies, corals being a typical example. You will have heard of coral reefs, and the same material in a fossil form exists today in the limestone of the Pennines. Limestone may also be formed by deposition from lime-rich sea water which has been subjected to evaporation.

As we have seen, fossils may form an important part of a sedimentary rock, but just what are they? Fossils are the remains, or some other evidence, of life which once existed on this planet. Under normal circumstances fossils usually represent the hard, preservable part of a prehistoric organism.

Unfortunately, the evolution of life did not develop creatures with hard skeletal parts, which could be fossilized, until around 600 million years ago; consequently it is chiefly in sedimentary rocks younger than this that fossils are to be found.

Early forms of life existed in the seas and consequently when they died their remains fell to the sea bed, later to become entombed in sedimentary rocks.

The relationship that fossils have with sedimentary rocks has enabled geologists to use them as an aid to dating rock formations. Now let us consider Britain's sedimentary rocks.

Few sedimentary rocks of Precambrian Age exist in Britain and for the most part it is difficult to date them. However, the Torridonian sandstones of North-West Scotland have a prominent place in British geology, being the oldest sedimentary rocks in the country.

If we turn back the clock to the Cambrian Period most, if not all of Britain was underwater and sediments were being laid down on a sea-floor which was slowly subsiding.

Such life as existed at this time was confined to the sea, and in the shallow waters several different types of creatures were thriving. Trilobites, which are much sought after today in a fossil form, were numerous and may have represented over 50 per cent of the fauna. However, brachiopods, sponges, worms, cystoids and graptolites were also present. A mild climate existed throughout the area.

The nearest land mass lay to the north-west, and the sediments being laid down undoubtedly originated from this area.

Unfortunately, as is the case with most rocks created hundreds of millions of years ago, erosion since their formation has all but obliterated them from the scene. However, sandstones and shales of Cambrian Age do outcrop in North Wales and South-East Ireland, but not in any great quantities. The limestone of Durness in Scotland, and the rocks of Skiddaw in the Lake District, are thought to have originated at this time.

The sea covering Britain narrowed during Ordovician times, as the sea floor began to buckle with the onset of the Caledonian Orogeny, but sediments were still being laid down. Today, sedimentary rocks of Ordovician Age still exist in West Wales, the Lake District and Scotland.

It is in Southern Scotland that the bulk of these rocks occur and in fact they extend in a large belt from Stranraer, north-eastwards past Sanquhar and Leadhills almost to Dunbar. They are broken near Merrick by a large mass of granite, and other intrusive igneous rocks dissect the Ordovician strata to the north-east. Shales, conglomerates, limestones and sandstones form the major part of these sedimentary rocks.

Trilobites and graptolites were amongst the most prolific creatures of the day but seaweeds, brachiopods, cystoids, corals and gastropods were also abundant.

The Silurian Period followed the Ordovician and sediments were still being deposited, although the old sea trough which covered most of Central Britain was narrowing as the sediments accumulated. Large masses of shale containing graptolites were formed, and limestone with coral reefs was created around the edge of the narrowing trough.

Life within the waters continued, becoming more diverse. The first fishes are believed to have existed towards the end of this short period.

Today, you will find the remains of the Silurian sediments in Central and West Wales, the east of Ireland and Southern Scotland, close to the Ordovician rocks already described.

The main folding movements, and the volcanic action of the Caledonian Orogeny, brought the Silurian Period to a close and opened the Devonian, or Old Red Sandstone, Period. The trough, which once covered most of Britain, had altered considerably, and most of Eastern and Central England was out of the water, as were the Southern Uplands of Scotland and the Grampians. Cornwall, Devon and South Wales were still under water along with most of Ireland and North-East Scotland.

The areas now above sea level were being subjected to erosion and rock debris was being laid down under the sea. Obviously the name Old Red Sandstone gives a clue to the nature of the rock which was characteristic of the time.

This was the age of fishes and the seas were teeming with them. The main varieties were the armoured, or bony fishes, although sharks had put in their first appearance. Trilobites were still common, but were starting the long decline to extinction. The graptolites had gone, but corals, sponges, lamellibranchs and gastropods were present in great numbers. Some insect life had appeared and the first amphibians were not long away.

Today Devonian sedimentary rocks can be found in the south-west in Cornwall and Devon, in Southern Ireland and in Central Scotland where they are intermixed with volcanic rocks. If we continue to the north-east we find rocks of the same age along the Moray Firth, on the Black Isle and in Caithness.

The Caithness sandstones, which are called flagstones because they are ideal for building purposes, are extensive and contain numerous fossils of the bony fishes. However, probably the best known location for fish fossils is Dura Den in Fife, where they occur in rocks of the same age.

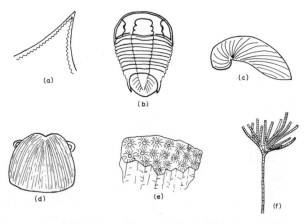

Fig. 19 Fossils may be found in many sedimentary rocks. (a) A graptolite. These creatures lived from the Upper Cambrian to the Lower Silurian. (b) A trilobite. Examples of trilobites may be found in rocks from the Lower Cambrian to the Lower Carboniferous. (c) Gryphaea, sometimes called 'devil's toe nail'. This is a member of the lamellibranch family. Gryphaea may be found in rocks from Jurassic to Eocene. (d) Linoproductus. This was a brachiopod which lived during the Carboniferous and Permian Periods. (e) Corals. Corals first existed in the Precambrian Period and advanced forms still exist today. (f) A crinoid. Crinoids existed from the Ordovician Period until recent times and are related to the sea lily.

The Caledonian Orogeny proceeded at a fair pace and the earlier sedimentary deposits were folded over into anticlines and synclines. These are simply the upward and downward folding of rocks which result in the original horizontal strata of the sediments being rearranged at peculiar angles.

The end of the Old Red Sandstone Period saw the Caledonian Mountains being heavily eroded. Sedimentary deposits were being formed in the oceans which now covered some of Scotland and most of England and Ireland. Consequently the bulk of Britain was under the water.

The lower part of the Carboniferous Period is given to the Carboniferous or Mountain Limestone and this rock, which was laid down in fairly shallow water, is now prominent in the Pennines, Central Scotland and Ireland.

Fossils are abundant in the limestone and a careful study of these has enabled geologists to divide the limestone into numerous zones. The trilobites finally became extinct at this time, but the corals were thriving, and these had been joined by the crinoids. These creatures were not unlike the sea lily of today, having a long stem made up of columnals, with a crown or 'flower' at the top, and a root at the bottom. Some of these creatures were free-moving and drifted about in large colonies. In Derbyshire, where fossile crinoids are abundant, they are called Derbyshire Screws.

By this time much of Central England and Southern Scotland was under water, but the uplifting of the Scottish continent in the north had encouraged erosion to take place more rapidly, and this resulted in large quantities of rock debris being washed southwards. The day of the Carboniferous Limestone was gone and Millstone Grit times lay ahead.

Coarse gritstones and shales were formed from the deltaic deposits of a great river which drained down from the Caledonian Continent, and slowly but surely, the Carboniferous sea began to silt up.

The Millstone Grit forms much of the Pennines today and in Derbyshire was used extensively for grindstones in the cutlery industry. Unfortunately the material was not highly suitable for this purpose and many stones fractured in use, killing and maiming the grinders who used them.

15. *Limestone often contains fossils. The specimen illustrated is a crinoidal limestone from the Peak District of Derbyshire. Size 130 × 85 mm.*

16. *Most sedimentary rocks are stratified. This photograph illustrates the gentle tilting strata in the flagstones at Thurso, Caithness.*

By now the sea was very shallow and large areas of mud and grit banks were above water level. Here, spores wafted southwards from the Scottish continent, landed and gave birth to life. Thus the great Carboniferous coal forests were born. The subsequent decaying and compressing of the vegetation eventually created the coal which today, along with some sandstones and shales, forms the series of rocks geologists call the Coal Measures.

17. The formation of coal. An artist's impression of a carboniferous coal forest. This photograph is reproduced by courtesy of the Director of the Institute of Geological Sciences. NERC copyright.

The Hercynian earth movements brought the Carboniferous Period to a close, but not before life, in the form of the amphibians, had struggled out of the water to place a tentative foot on dry land.

Hot, arid desert conditions began to set in throughout Britain as the rain-bearing winds were diverted by the uplifting of much of Southern England, Wales, the Pennines and the Lake District. The Permian Period was characterized by the formation of red marls, which are clayey, lime-rich sediments. Later a large inland sea developed which extended between North-East England and Poland, in which the formation of the Magnesian, or Dolomitic Limestone took place. Today this limestone outcrops on the coast of Durham and extends southwards into Yorkshire, eventually reaching as far south as Nottingham. The Magnesian Limestone occurs in two varieties, one made up of small spherical oolites, while the other is the famous cannon-ball limestone. The latter is composed of cannon-ball-like concretions which are up to 127 mm (5 in) in diameter.

18. 'The Painted Desert'. An artist's impression of part of the Lake District (Eden Valley) during the Permian Period. This photograph is reproduced by courtesy of the Director of the Institute of Geological Sciences. NERC copyright.

The Triassic Period followed the Permian, and probably the most famous 'rocks' from this period are the Bunter Pebble Beds which, together with sandstones, outcrops in the Midlands and on the south coast at Budleigh Salterton.

Still in the Triassic Period, the next rocks to be formed were the Keuper sandstones, but conditions were to change. The water covering Britain began to retreat under the effect of the hot arid conditions and this resulted in the creation of a series of shallow lakes.

19. Cannon-ball limestone. This rock is formed of cannon-ball-like concretions and may be found at several localities in the Permian rocks of Durham. Size 165 × 130 mm.

The lakes were undoubtedly brackish, and evaporation rapidly reduced the level of water. As the water content became lower, so the salt become richer, until a stage was reached at which the salt could not be contained in solution and it was precipitated to the bed of the lake. When all the water finally evaporated, all that was left were the great masses of salt and gypsum which have considerable economic importance in Cheshire and Durham today.

Marine conditions returned to Britain towards the end of the Triassic, and limestones were laid down, including the famous Cotham Marble which has been worked near Bristol for ornamental purposes. The term marble has frequently been used to describe ornamental limestones which have no connection with the metamorphic rocks of the same name.

The Triassic Period was the dawn of the Age of Reptiles, and many dinosaurs were prowling the landscape.

At the beginning of the Jurassic Period, shales, clays and limestones were being deposited. These included the fossil-bearing shales of Whitby and Charmouth. The former locality is famous for jet and alum, both of which were formed during this period. Ammonites and belemnites are the most notable fossils to be found in these rocks.

20. *This ammonite has been preserved in pyrite and is from the Jurassic shales of Charmouth in Dorset. Size 1·5 cm diameter.*

As the Jurassic continued oolitic limestones were being deposited in the clear, warm waters of a shallow sea, much of England and Ireland being under the water at this time.

Today, rocks formed during the Lower (Liassic) and Middle Jurassic Period extend side by side in a long line from Dorset to Yorkshire.

21. *The cliffs at Charmouth are composed of Jurassic (Liassic) shales. The shales contain many fossils including the bones of the famous dinosaurs.*

Later the seas receded to the east, and on becoming very muddy gave rise to the Oxford and Kimmeridge clays. However, a brief period of clear marine conditions prevailed, resulting in the formation of coral and oolitic limestones between the clays. These limestones are collectively called the Corallian. The last rocks of importance to be formed during the Jurassic were the Portland beds which include the famous Purbeck Marble. However, the Upper Purbeck Beds belong to the Cretaceous.

By now the reptiles were becoming masters not only of the land, but also of the sea and the air. Dinosaur fossils are rare, but they do occur in the shales of Charmouth, and dinosaur footprints have been found in rocks on the shore at Burniston, near Scarborough.

(a)   (b)

Fig. 20 Examples of two fossils which can be found in rocks of Jurassic and Cretaceous Times. These are: (a) a coiled ammonite; (b) the long pointed shield of a belemnite.

The Cretaceous Period, which began 140 million years ago, is best remembered for the white Chalk rock, which today forms the wolds of Yorkshire and Lincolnshire and the Wealden Area in the south-east. It is considered that the Chalk seas were clear and warm and that on land conditions were arid. The Chalk was preceded by the deposition of a variety of clays and greensand; however, to all but the academic, Chalk is the only noticeable rock.

Belemnites, ammonites, crinoids and echinoids, the latter including the sea urchin, thrived in the shallow waters. Flint is particularly common in the Chalk and often the fossils are preserved within it.

This was the last fling for the great dinosaurs which had been masters of the world for almost 200 million years. Their extinction has been attributed to a variety of reasons including the cooling of the climate and a change in the nature of the vegetation. Whatever the reason, they had been a highly effective life form and we shall probably never know why they were swept away upon the cool winds of the Tertiary.

The passing of these reptiles allowed the mammals to escape from their obscurity, and paved the way for the 'ascent of man'.

Fig. 21 *A map showing the areas affected by the Alpine earth movements of the Tertiary.*

The name Tertiary was created in conjunction with a now outdated classification of rocks, and has been divided into five subdivisions, or epochs. Of these the Palaeocene is represented in the rocks of Britain by the Thanet sands; the Eocene is characterized in the sandstones and clays of the London and Hampshire basin; the Oligocene is to be found in the coral limestones of Hampshire; while the Miocene is not represented in the rock pages of Britain's history. Finally, the Pliocene was essentially a period of erosion and the only rocks of this age are confined to East Anglia.

It is at this point that the story of Britain's sedimentary rocks comes to an end, but erosion is still at work and tomorrow's sedimentary rocks are being formed today. Glacial deposits are of a sedimentary character but the story of the Pleistocene Ice Age belongs to another chapter.

The formation of minerals in sedimentary rocks

Weathering

The effects of weathering on rock formations can be very severe and may result in the formation of new minerals. The weathering of a mineral vein may cause its constituents to break down into secondary minerals. Pyrite is a good example, for on weathering it may break down into hematite or limonite.

Calcite is dissolved out of limestone by running water, subsequently to be redeposited as stalactites, stalagmites or coatings on the walls of caves.

Evaporation

We have already seen how the evaporation of water may lead to the formation of mineral deposits, and typical minerals formed in this way are salt, gypsum, and anhydrite.

Magmatic formation of minerals

I have already explained how minerals can be deposited from mineral-rich solutions and gases which emanate from hot masses of cooling rock within the earth. Mineralization of this type may occur in all rocks including those termed sedimentary. Mineral veins are common in limestone due to the fact that limestone is easily dissolved and replaced by minerals from hot solutions emanating from much deeper down in the earth's crust.

The Geological Time Scale showing the characteristic sedimentary rocks formed during each period.

PERIOD	MILLIONS OF YEARS SINCE START OF PERIOD	TYPICAL ROCKS FORMED
Quaternary	2	Soft sand and clay
Tertiary	65	Limestone; shell and pebble beds; sand and clay
Cretaceous	140	Clay; sandstone and chalk
Jurassic	195	Shale; clay, limestone and sandstone
Triassic	230	Red marl, sandstone and evaporite
Permian	280	Marl, conglomerate, sandstone and magnesian limestone
Carboniferous	345	
Coal Measures		Sandstone, shale and coal
Millstone Grit		Gritstones, sandstone, shale and coal
Carboniferous Limestone		Limestone, shale, dolomite and coal
Devonian (Old Red Sandstone)	395	Red sandstone, grit, shale and conglomerate
Silurian	435	Shale, siltstone, limestone and sandstone
Ordovician	500	Slate, shale and gritstones
Cambrian	570	Shale, sandstone and slate
Precambrian	Undefined	Shale, gritstones, sandstone and conglomerate

CHAPTER FIVE

MINERALS IN BRITAIN'S SEDIMENTARY ROCKS

Scotland

It is the high road to the far north of Scotland that we must first traverse, for we are bound for the country of Caithness. Here amongst the beautiful fertile countryside of this, the least typical of the Highland counties, we find that lead and zinc ores have been mined in some quantity. Achanarras near to Halkirk has been the scene of mining for lead and zinc, and copper ores were once worked in sandstone of Devonian Age at Castle of Old Wick. Hematite in a vein form was exploited in the nineteenth century near Reay, also in Caithness.

From Caithness it is a short step to the Orkneys and here we find that ores of lead and zinc have been worked on South Ronaldsay and at Stromness on the Orkney Mainland. Malachite, the green copper ore, has been identified on the minute Fair Isle.

The Devonian sedimentary rocks of Shetland are credited with malachite and fluorite, both of which occur near Sandwich. However, the Shetlands are mainly hewn out of metamorphic rocks which do not concern us here.

Moving southwards on to the Scottish mainland we find comparatively little evidence of sedimentary rocks in Sutherland, but the Jurassic sediments of the east coast offer an interesting range of fossils. Also on the east coast near Dunrobin

Castle at Golspie, amethyst and smoky quartz can be found in a vein, cutting a conglomerate.

Sedimentary Rocks

Triassic

Permian

Coal Measures ⎫
Millstone Grit ⎬ Carboniferous
Carboniferous Limestone ⎭

Devonian

Silurian

Ordovician

Cambrian

Precambrian

Igneous and Metamorphic Rocks

Fig. 22 The sedimentary rocks of Scotland.

Passing from Sutherland into Ross and Cromarty we find that bornite, brockantite and malachite, all copper ores, have been found at Rassal, near Kishorn. South of the Great Glen in Inverness-shire, sedimentary rocks are mainly confined to the coastal plain and it is at Lossiemouth on the Moray Firth that we must pay our next call. Here we find galena, the principal ore of lead, and learn that it was once mined in some considerable quantity. Baryte can be located in limestone at Balfreish near Nairn and fluorite is to be found in a rather unusual situation near Elgin. Here fluorite is not present in a mineral vein, but forms the matrix in sandstone, having replaced the original bonding mineral. A similar situation exists in nearby Moray-shire at Greenbrae Quarry, where fluorite occurs as the matrix in similar Permian sandstones. Green Crystals of this mineral exist at Inverugie in the same area.

Fluorspar is also common amongst the sedimentary rocks of Aberdeenshire and is well known alongside galena, calcite and sphalerite in quarry workings at Crathie and Abergairn. Blue fluorite has been reported in Glen Muick. Further south we find that the Loch Tay limestones by Loch Fyne, in Argyll, also contain fluorite together with the copper ores, particularly malachite. These limestones have been quarried extensively for building stone, and exposures of rock are correspondingly numerous.

To find the next major occurrence of minerals amongst sedimentary rocks in the Highlands, we have to move further to the west across the igneous rocks of the Lorne Plateau, out to the Isle of Islay. The Islay limestone and the Esknish slates have both been penetrated by mineral veins. Galena, sphalerite, pyrite and chalcopyrite are the principal mineral ores, but some lesser minerals also occur. Chalcopyrite, the copper ore, has been exploited intermittently at the Kilsleven Mine on Islay but little activity has gone on here since 1860.

Moving south-eastwards we enter Scotland's Midland Valley, which is the area surrounding the Rivers Forth and Clyde. Here sedimentary rocks form the bulk of the landscape, but despite this they rarely contain minerals, and it is not until we enter the southern uplands that minerals become abundant again.

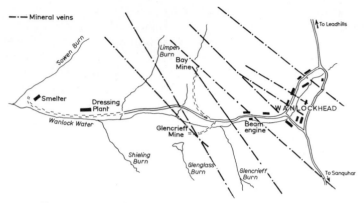

Fig. 23 A map showing the mineral veins at Wanlockhead.

The barren moorland scenery of Southern Scotland is carved out of Ordovician and Silurian sediments and here, nestling amongst the hills, we find a small village called Leadhills. It is the presence of galena, the principal ore of lead, which has so firmly stamped itself on this area, and mining has been carried out here for at least 700 years. Two miles to the west of Leadhills is the village of Wanlockhead where sphalerite has been mined in quantity since 1880. The major minerals in the Leadhills area are not exhausted, large reserves still remaining in the ground. The last attempt to extract mineral ores took place back in 1957, but surveys reappraising the situation are carried out quite regularly. Certainly, it will be no surprise if in the near future we hear that one of the larger mining companies has reopened the major workings here.

Spoil heaps left behind by previous mining activities are numerous and a wide range of good quality mineral specimens can be found. Finds here include galena, sphalerite, fluorite (usually colourless), chalcopyrite, malachite, chrysocolla, pyrite, quartz, calcite and hemimorphite, which occurs in blue and yellow. Hematite occurs on the mine dumps, and much of this would appear to have been created by the weathering of pyrite. Recently rhodonite, the pink manganese ore, has been credited to the area, while gold was panned from Glengaber Burn, by St Mary's Loch, way back in the sixteenth century.

22. Spoil heaps are a common site in mining areas. The mine workings illustrated are the remains of the Glencrieff Mine at Wanlockhead.

Silver was a profitable by-product of the galena smelting operations, but this interesting mineral is not present on spoil heaps in an uncombined form. Jamesonite, a lead mineral containing antimony, was also extracted at Leadhills, but a more important site has been the Glendinning Mine, between Langholm and Eskdalemuir, where stilbite, together with galena, jamesonite and sphalerite have been extracted from shale.

Barytes occur in the sedimentary rocks near Auchencairn in Kirkcudbrightshire and in several places further south along the coast, but now we are almost in England.

England and Wales

Sedimentary rocks play a much more important role in the structure of England and Wales, and mineral occurrences are quite numerous. Consequently, we shall stick to the major mineral-rich areas.

The first area we arrive at as we move southwards is the Lake District. Here amongst the Carboniferous Limestone of Cumbria, we find one mineral being extracted in economical proportions; the mineral is hematite.

This mineral is not particularly attractive, but in the form of specularite, which is to be found here, it is at its most desirable as a mineral specimen. The less attractive Kidney ore is also obtained here with smoky quartz, fluorite and baryte. Egremont is the main centre for hematite but there are several quarries in the area where hematite, calcite and quartz may be found. Gypsum has been worked where it occurs amongst the Eden Shales near Carlisle.

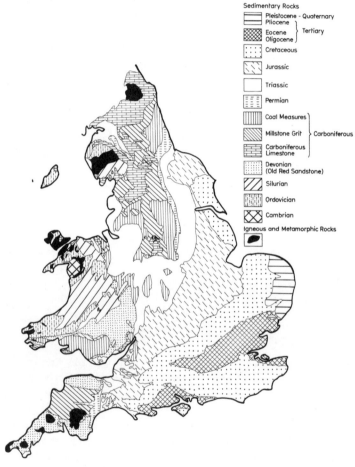

Sedimentary Rocks

Pleistocene - Quaternary
Pliocene ⎫
Eocene ⎬ Tertiary
Oligocene ⎭
Cretaceous
Jurassic
Triassic
Permian
Coal Measures ⎫
Millstone Grit ⎬ Carboniferous
Carboniferous Limestone ⎭
Devonian (Old Red Sandstone)
Silurian
Ordovician
Cambrian

Igneous and Metamorphic Rocks

Fig. 24 The sedimentary rocks in England and Wales.

Leaving the Lake District behind and moving to the east, we find that clay ironstone (siderite) was once mined in Durham and Cleveland; but this industry has now passed away and the next important mineral-rich area is in view.

The Pennine Hills dominate the scenery of Central and Northern England and are a great source of mineral specimens. It is in the Carboniferous Limestone, and to a lesser extent the Millstone Grit, that the mineral veins occur. The mineral-bearing rocks outcrop in Durham, the Yorkshire Dales and the Peak District, and in each area mining has gone on for many years. Certainly minerals have been extracted in the Pennines since before Roman times, but only in a small way.

Galena was the most important mineral mined in the past but today the accent has changed and it is fluorite and baryte which are being mined. Fluorite is used to make hydrofluoric acid, and baryte has application as a filler in paint.

23. Galena is the principal ore of lead and has been mined in many parts of Britain. This specimen is from Blanchland, Northumberland. Size 60 × 40 mm.

In Durham, quartz is the main gangue mineral and interesting crystal specimens occur on most mine dumps. Vein agate may also be found here. Calcite and witherite are the other major minerals although secondary minerals are important at specific locations.

24. *Baryte is barium sulphate. It is common on mine dumps in old lead mining areas. Size 130 × 110 mm.*

25. *Sphalerite or zinc blende is here seen with the white mineral baryte. This specimen is from Skiddaw in the Lake District. Size 80 × 60 mm.*

It is fluorite which holds pride of place here in Durham. Beautiful crystal specimens have been a common find in the area, and are perhaps best represented by the famous green crystals from Heights Quarry in Weardale. Yellow fluorite dominates the mineral scene in the Yorkshire Dales where barytocalcite, calamine, hydrozincite and smithsonite can be added to the mineral collector's list. Wharfedale, Nidderdale, Swaledale, Arkengarthdale and Teesdale were the main mining areas, and old mine dumps are a common sight.

26. Fluorspar may be found in beautiful crystal specimens. The specimen illustrated is green fluorspar from Weardale. Size 70 × 60 mm.

In Derbyshire, fluorite again takes pride of place through the presence of the unique Blue John. This attractive gemstone, which has been used extensively for ornaments and jewellery, is to be found on the Treak Cliff at Castleton, although good quality material is scarce today. The mines where this stone is extracted are open to the public and make an interesting excursion.

Purple and yellow fluorspar crystals, which are sometimes large, can be found in Smalldale, and with natural pitch in Pindale; while baryte, calcite, galena and more rarely sphalerite are to be located without much difficulty in the Castleton area. Hydrocarbon minerals have been identified at Windy Knoll. A rather unusual form of baryte called oakstone has been found in the past at Arbor Low. This stone resembles wood and good pieces represent the complete cross section of a tree trunk;

however, it is not to be confused with fossil wood with which it has no connection. The true location of the site at Arbor Low is not common knowledge today, but the material still finds its way into dealers' shops.

27 Blue John is a banded form of massive fluorite which occurs in the Treak Cliff at Castleton in Derbyshire. Siz 80 × 65 mm.

28. The Winnat's Pass at Castleton in Derbyshire is the home of the famous Blue John. The stone has been used extensively for ornamental purposes and supplies are now said to be scarce.

Bornite, malachite and azurite, together with chalcopyrite, are to be found in the Matlock area, but the prime site for these minerals is by the copper mines at Ecton Hill on the Staffordshire border. It must be pointed out that the malachite to be found here, or anywhere else in Britain, is not usually of the gemstone variety.

In the sedimentary rocks of the Yorkshire and Derbyshire Pennines, quartz is not present in its crystalline forms but is represented by chert, which exists as bands in the limestone. In the chert it is possible to find small pockets of gemstone material, especially agate, chalcedony and opal, although the latter is rarely opalescent.

Both opal and agate have been located amongst the chert in Swaledale in Yorkshire and at Glebe Mine and Friden in Derbyshire. At the latter locality the agate is found in the form, beekite, where it occurs as a replacement in the remains of fossils.

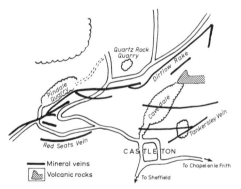

Fig. 25 A map showing the mineral veins around Castleton in Derbyshire.

Before leaving Derbyshire it would not be right to omit some mention of the numerous limestones which under the name marble won considerable fame back in the last century, when they were employed for ornamental purposes.

A great many beautiful vases, snuff boxes, table tops and even fireplaces were manufactured from these limestones, specimens of which can still be found today. The black marble (limestone) from Ashford was perhaps the most beautiful; but there was the bird's eye marble from Wetton, which was a fossil limestone; the rosewood marble from Nettlerdale and the Duke's red marble from Alport. All the Duke's red marble was extracted from the mine at Alport on the demand of the Duke of Devonshire and today exists in the cellars at Chatsworth House.

Before moving on southwards we must pause momentarily by the sea, at Whitby. Here, amidst the Jurassic shales, we find an interesting gemstone. Jet is the name and, not surprisingly, black is the colour, of this once popular material. It takes a reasonably high polish and in the middle of the last century was popular for mourning jewellery.

Once extensive, the jet jewellery industry is now almost dead, although it is popular with local amateur lapidaries. The material was extracted from several sites near Robin Hood's Bay. By nature, jet is a hard compact form of lignite and can be recognized easily, as it looks like coal, but does not soil the hand.

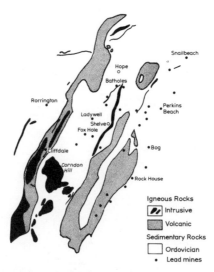

Fig. 26 A geological map showing the mining area in Shropshire.

Leaving the coast of Yorkshire behind, we must bear to the west and slightly south for Cheshire.

Rock salt or halite occurs in vast quantities amongst the flat fertile scenery of Cheshire, but is of little interest to the collector, although selenite crystals also occur here. Perhaps more interesting are the copper minerals, including azurite and malachite, that occur at Alderley Edge.

Further south we come to the Welsh border. Here among Silurian sedimentary rocks we can see yet more evidence of past mining activities. The villages of Shelve and Snailbeach are at the centre of a once productive mining industry which is now over. As we found in the Pennines, galena, sphalerite and baryte are the most common minerals, but calcite, quartz and occasionally chalcedony are the unwanted or gangue materials.

Baryte, malachite and chalcocite are to be expected to the south of Habberley, where they were once mined in a small way. Baryte has also been worked near Breidden Hill.

Turning to the west we enter Wales and in the north we find that mineralization has again taken place. It is the Carboniferous Limestone which has been invaded by mineral-rich solutions. Galena and sphalerite are the main minerals, but silver has been extracted in small quantities. Other minerals found here include chalcopyrite, fluorite and baryte. The most important areas where mineralization has taken place are near Minera, a village near Wrexham, and on Halkyn Mountain.

In Central and South Wales we find the same story, where the Carboniferous Limestone has undergone mineralization. The lead and zinc minerals are again prominent, but copper, iron ores, silver and gold have been extracted in worthwhile amounts.

Dyffryn, west of Aberystwyth in Cardiganshire, was a profitable place for lead and silver, and the gold came from Ogofau near Llandovery. Hematite also occurs in the limestone and has been exploited commercially at the Lanharry Mine.

On the south coast of Wales, just to the east of Tenby we find Wiseman's Bridge, and here quartz crystals and calcite occur, the latter in concretionary nodules. The crystals occur in the cliffs, and the nodules are to be found among the shingle.

Turning to the east we traverse South Wales, stopping briefly at Penarth near Cardiff where gypsum in the form of orange alabaster can be found on the beach, before crossing the Severn Road Bridge back into England.

29. Calcite, which is calcium carbonate, is a common mineral in most mining areas. It occurs in many forms including the dog-tooth crystals illustrated. This specimen is from Wells in Somerset. Size 112 × 100 mm.

The Mendip Hills are carved out of Carboniferous Limestone, and galena has been mined there since Roman times. Fluorite, baryte and calcite were the principal gangue minerals. Some silver was also obtained from the smelting of the galena.

Baryte has been worked in the Carboniferous Limestone near Bridgwater; and calamine, which is zinc carbonate, has been extracted from the Dolomitic Conglomerate, which overlies the Carboniferous Limestone around the edge of the Mendip Hills. The centre of the zinc mining was at the village of Rowbarrow. The same conglomerate gave up pyrolusite, the black manganese ore, at several places in the Mendips including East Harptree, Wadbury and Croscombe, but mining has now ceased.

Red Marls of Triassic Age also outcrop around the Mendips, and are famous for the geodes, or potato stones, they contain. The potato stones may be lined with calcite or quartz crystals, the latter occasionally being represented by purple amethyst. Agate patterns may also occur in the centre of these concretionary nodules.

Yate, north of Bristol, is famous for the presence of celestite, where it occurs in the Keuper Marl. This mineral, like the rock salt of Cheshire, may be formed by evaporation and is frequently associated with dolomite and gypsum.

Moving westwards into Devon we find marcasite and malachite with silver, zinc and lead minerals at the Coombe Martin mines near Ilfracombe.

On the South Coast we find a variety of fossils, many preserved in pyrite, in the Jurassic shales of Charmouth, together with calcite which occurs in concretionary nodules. Rock crystal, chalcedony and agate occur on the same stretch of beach in chert pebbles.

As we move away to the east the sedimentary rocks become younger and younger while at the same time they become less and less productive of interesting minerals.

Marcasite occurs in the chalk cliffs of Dover in Kent, and with selenite at Folkestone. At Mountfield, in the same area, we find deposits of anhydrite and gypsum. Selenite, baryte and pyrite have been found at Sheppey, but this part of Britain is very deficient in interesting and desirable minerals.

Ireland

The province of Northern Ireland is dominated by the igneous rocks we have already considered and consequently our path lies southwards into the Republic.

We find evidence of the extraction of lead and zinc ores near Navan which is on the border between Silurian and Carboniferous sediments, the latter being the famous Carboniferous Limestone, which in fact covers much of Central Ireland.

South of Dublin, beyond the Wicklow Mountains, we find the remains of more mining activity, and galena, chalcedony and copper ores, including chalcopyrite, may be found at Glendalough Mine. At Avoca, a few miles further south, we find galena, sphalerite, pyrite, chalcopyrite and tetrahedrite.

In the south-west we find that azurite and malachite, together with the other copper ores, occur at Kenmare near Killarney, and the same minerals with baryte are known at Ballycummisk. Quartz crystals, sometimes amethyst or citrine, occur in veins which cut the Devonian rocks of counties Cork and Kerry.

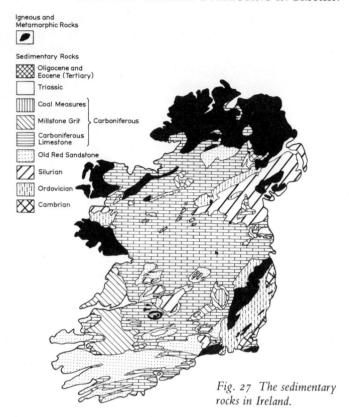

Igneous and
Metamorphic Rocks

Sedimentary Rocks
Oligocene and
Eocene (Tertiary)
Triassic
Coal Measures
Millstone Grit   } Carboniferous
Carboniferous
Limestone
Old Red Sandstone
Silurian
Ordovician
Cambrian

*Fig. 27 The sedimentary
rocks in Ireland.*

North of Killarney the Devonian or Old Red Sandstone sediments give way to Millstone Grit, and it is not until we move back on to the Carboniferous Limestone at Ennis, in County Clare, that we find minerals again.

Cassiterite and galena occur at the Killbracken Mine at Castletown, and smithsonite at the nearby Sheshodonnel mine, while hemimorphite, baryte and galena occur at the Silvermines near Killaloe. Gortdrum and Tynagh in the same area are the home of numerous minerals including chalcopyrite, cinnabar, baryte, azurite, malachite, cerussite, pyromorphite and galena.

Finally, further north at Abbey Town in Sligo we find bitumen, calcite and dolomite, while sphalerite and baryte occur at Benbullen.

Calcite and quartz are the major gangue minerals in most mining areas, and as such have not been specifically mentioned with relation to every site at which they occur. Calcite, not surprisingly, occurs widely in limestone where quartz is not as common; however, when quartz does occur, such gemstones as amethyst, chalcedony and agate are possible finds.

CHAPTER SIX

NEW ROCKS FROM OLD

As you drive around Britain's countryside you will see many different rock formations, and come up against many different types of rock. The appearance of these rocks, even when seen from a distance, can offer the experienced collector a clue to their identity.

If you see an outcrop of metamorphic rock, it should be identifiable by its strongly banded or contorted appearance. Metamorphic rocks are created when the earth is in its most violent mood. They occur when sedimentary, igneous rocks or older metamorphic rocks are trapped within the earth, and subjected to great heat and pressure. The metamorphic rocks of the Scottish Highlands were once of a sedimentary nature, but at the time of the Caledonian Orogeny they were modified, deep within the earth's crust.

These rocks were trapped between opposing forces, which were striving to create a new mountain chain. The processes of metamorphism are quite capable of changing rocks of any character into something quite new. It is not however envisaged that the rock ever became liquid under the influence of these forces, but they probably became 'plastic'.

The character of the original rock is lost, as its mineral constituents recrystallize. Of course the amount of heat and pressure to which the rocks are subjected can vary and this decides the degree to which they are altered. A rock which has undergone only slight metamorphism will probably not appear greatly changed. On the other hand one which has been subjected to the full wrath of the earth's forces will not in any way resemble its former character.

Today geologists can trace the modification of a rock through all the gradations that can occur. Let us consider shale as an example. When subjected to a little heat and pressure, shale will be transformed to slate. Further metamorphism will transform the slate to phyllite, but now the grades of the metamorphic process are characterized by the most prominent mineral the rocks contain. In phyllite, chlorite is the most predominant mineral.

The next stages take us on to mica schist and kyanite schist where mica and then kyanite are the prominent minerals. The metamorphism needed to create the kyanite schist is greater than that to create garnet, so we also have a garnetiferous mica schist. A still greater degree of heat and pressure will transform the kyanite schist into schists containing the mineral sillimanite. At this point the schist series ends and it is generally considered that further metamorphism may produce the rocks called gneiss.

The examination of metamorphic rocks has enabled geologists to identify the original rock from which they were created. A peridotite rock rich in olivine can become serpentine. A limestone after metamorphism can become marble. However, the name marble is often used to describe serpentine and decorative limestones which are not true marbles.

When metamorphism attacks granite it will eventually become transformed into gneiss, while the lowly sandstone becomes compacted together into a quartzite. It is now considered that some granites may have a metamorphic background, and it has been suggested that any rock subjected to heat and pressure will ultimately strive to become granite. This process is called 'granitization'.

Should large masses of rock be folded within the earth, then metamorphism will take place on a large scale, and this is called regional metamorphism. However, metamorphism may also take place on a smaller scale, when it is called contact metamorphism.

When molten rock passes along fissures in the earth's crust, the heat from the magma bakes and transforms the rocks on either side of the fissure and metamorphism can again take place. The amount of rock affected, i.e. the metamorphic aureole, can vary depending upon the size of the igneous body. Now we must consider the metamorphic rocks which occur in Britain.

For the first time we find the existence of rocks in Britain which go back far beyond the 600 million year limit we have had to set ourselves in the preceding chapters.

To consider the formation of Britain's earliest metamorphic rocks we shall have to travel to the north-west of Scotland, to the Isle of Lewis in the Outer Hebrides. Here we find the grandfather of all the rocks in the British Isles, the Lewisian Gneiss. This rock has been dated somewhat tentatively as being around 3,000 million years old, and was metamorphosed in days of which we have precious little record. The bulk of the gneiss is thought to have been of igneous origin, but a small amount was sedimentary. Today the gneiss occurs, not only in the Outer Hebrides from where it takes its name, but also on the Scottish mainland.

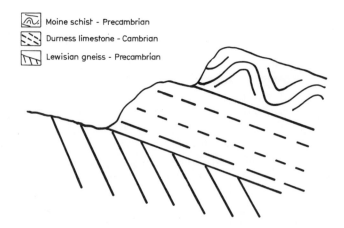

Moine schist - Precambrian
Durness limestone - Cambrian
Lewisian gneiss - Precambrian

Fig. 28 A simplified diagram of the rocks at Knockan Cliff. The youngest rocks are in the centre.

Further east the Moine series of rocks, which are characterized by the Moine Schist, form a major part of the Northern Highlands, and are evidence of further upheaval within the earth. These rocks are substantially younger than the Lewisian Gneiss, but are still firmly entrenched in the Precambrian.

Due to the structured turmoil within the earth the rocks of the Moine series, after intensive buckling and folding, have been thrust over many younger rocks. This fascinating, if somewhat faint, chapter of Britain's history was first examined near Knockan in Ross-shire, and today is the scene of the geological nature trail at Knockan Cliff.

The nature trail reveals the various rocks which form the scenery in the area, and shows clearly how the much-altered schists directly overlie the Durness Limestone, which is almost totally unaltered. This association led several geologists to believe that the schist did not belong above the limestone and subsequently they were proved right.

While still in the Precambrian era we must now trek southwards into England and down to the south-west and Cornwall. The Lizard Headland is composed of metamorphic rocks which were created before the beginning of the Cambrian Period.

Originally the rocks of the Lizard were mudstones, sandstones and basaltic lavas, but today, metamorphism having taken its toll, mica schists, granulites and hornblende schists make up much of the rock scenery. However, we cannot overlook the large mass of serpentine which was created by the alteration of a peridotite intrusion.

Next we come to the ancient rocks of the Welsh Borderland. Like those of the Northern Highlands, the old rocks of Salop have been altered out of all recognition down the years. The metamorphic rocks are essentially schists and gneiss, and occur in some abundance around Church Stretton, Haughmond Hill near Shrewsbury, and near Rushton. These rocks are closely associated with the remains of aged volcanic rocks which form the nearby Wrekin.

The formation of metamorphic rocks on a large scale is dependent upon crustal deformation and this takes millions of years to occur. In addition it does not normally take place in rocks on the fringe of a mountain-building orogeny. It is chiefly confined to those deep in the heart of the tortured structure.

Consequently, we shall find if we now turn our attention to the last 600 million years that only on one occasion has Britain been at the heart of a major rock-moving catastrophe. The Hercynian and Alpine mountain-building episode did not affect Britain as greatly as did the Caledonian Orogeny of 400 million years ago.

Fig. 29   The metamorphic rocks of the Northern Highlands of Scotland.

The Caledonian Mountains extended from Wales and England through Scotland and across to Norway. However, the south was somewhat on the fringe of events and it is to the heart of the orogeny in Scotland that we must turn. The metamorphic rocks of the Grampian Highlands, which are characterized by mica schist, began their life as sediments which were laid down during the late Precambrian and early Cambrian Period. Their subsequent metamorphism took place at the very beginning of the Caledonian Orogeny, possibly during the Ordovician Period, and even earlier. Many grades of the metamorphism of sediments can be found here, but the less strongly metamorphosed sediments were transformed during late Silurian or early Old Red Sandstone times.

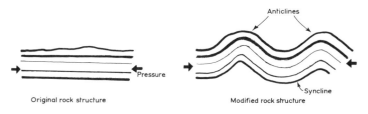

Anticlines

Pressure

Syncline

Original rock structure   Modified rock structure

Fig. 30 The formation of synclines and anticlines.

Regional metamorphism is almost entirely confined to the Highlands and in small amounts to Northern Ireland, although the slates of the Lake District and Wales are undoubtedly the result of shale hardening off under pressure in Silurian or Devonian times. Since the Caledonian Orogeny no intense regional metamorphism has taken place in the British Isles.

Contact metamorphism presents a different story. Wherever igneous intrusions or volcanoes have occurred contact metamorphism will have taken place. In the case of the large masses of granite which occur in the Cairngorms, or in Cornwall, the metamorphic aureole may be quite considerable, stretching up to several miles. On the other hand the aureole surrounding a dyke or sill may be a matter of a few feet. In some instances the metamorphism of the surrounding rock may be minimal while in others it may be extensive.

Metamorphic rocks occur in isolated bodies in Britain today, but it is more than possible that much of the country rests upon a platform of intensely altered rocks, as has been established in South Wales.

The formation of minerals in metamorphic rocks

Like the sedimentary rocks we have already discussed, veins of minerals may be formed by magmatic means, within metamorphic rocks. This is true of Cornwall where mineral ores have been found around the Killas, the metamorphosed sediments which surround the granite. Varying grades of metamorphism will result in the formation of different rocks and different minerals. Quartz, mica, kyanite and the many varieties of garnet are among the more common minerals, but tourmaline, staurolite, andalusite, sillimanite, epidote, idocrase and spinel may also be found. These minerals may exist simply as a rock constituent but crystals can occur in fissures in metamorphic rocks.

30. Mica is a common mineral in metamorphic rocks. It occurs as small leaves or plates. These specimens are from near Invershiel in Inverness-shire. Size (specimen on left) 35 × 25 mm.

The process of metamorphism can create some of the world's most beautiful minerals. It is only unfortunate that, in Britain, the specimens you may find will rarely be suitable for jewellery purposes. However, the alteration of such rocks as basalt and limestone has given rise to the formation of two gemstone materials, serpentine and marble. Both these stones are fairly widespread, and specimens may be easily found.

CHAPTER SEVEN

MINERALS IN BRITAIN'S METAMORPHIC ROCKS

If we turn to the geological map of Great Britain we find that metamorphic rocks are scarce in England, Wales and Ireland. Consequently our attention is drawn to the north, to the remains of the Caledonian Mountains which today form the Highlands of Scotland.

Scotland

Starting in the Northern Highlands, we find fluorite of a blue colour in the Lewisian Gneiss at Glen Logan, while garnets, kyanite and tourmaline are widespread throughout the area. Brucite marble occurs near Loch Assynt, probably as a result of the metamorphism of the Durness Limestone. Achnasheen is the site of a small quarry, where almandine garnet has been found in mica schist and fluorite again crops up on the east side of Carn Chuinneag in a biotite gneiss. Coming quickly southwards we find reference to kyanite in large blue crystals at Gortally, andalusite at An Cruachan and zircon together with serpentine north-west of Milton on Glen Urquhart.

South of the Great Glen and Fort William lies the village of Ballachulish where slate was worked over many years. Pyrite is a common find in the slate which has been reworked recently during a period of road widening in the area.

If we now turn to the west, to the Islands of the Hebrides, we find that metamorphic rocks are well represented, especially in the outer islands. Harris, of tweed fame, promptly springs to mind as the home of such gemstones as olivine and zircon, but the mountain of Chaipaval is also known for microcline feldspar, garnet, beryl and mica. The Isle of Tiree is a good site for serpentine which occurs with garnet, epidote, sphene and augite.

31. Brucite marble, pictured in the foreground, was formed by the metamorphism of the Durness Limestone. The hills in the background are composed of the igneous rock syenite.

Still on the islands we find that a very attractive marble has been formed where basalt has invaded limestone at Elgol, on Skye. This material occurs in a wide range of colours from white, through green, to pink and grey. Garnets may be found in the south of Skye near Armadale in the Lewisian Gneiss.

Baryte has been found on the Isle of Coll and marble of a serpentinous nature occurs on the sacred Isle of Iona. Crossing over to the Isle of Mull, we find kyanite and tourmaline in the Moine Schists to the south of Bunessan, close to the fringe of the Tertiary lavas.

Further to the west, at localities on the north and south banks of Loch Scridain, there occurs a rather rare mineral, sapphire. The sapphires of Mull were formed during the Tertiary Period, at the time of the igneous activity which affected most of the north-west of Scotland. It is believed that the sapphires were created when small blocks of aluminium-rich sedimentary rock were metamorphosed by an igneous intrusion. It has been said that the original sedimentary rock formed the roof of a great underground magma chamber, and that small blocks of this rock were broken off the roof and carried upward by the magma, as it was intruded into the rocks above, in the form of sills. In the academic world the limestone blocks are called xenoliths, the sapphires being contained within them. Localities for the sapphires include Scobul and Tiroran on the north bank of Loch Scridain, and there are several sites east of Bunessan on the south bank. Specimens which are extremely small occur on the south coast near the Carsaig Arches. None of the sapphires are suitable for lapidary work.

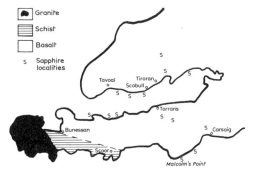

Fig. 31 A map showing the sapphire localities on the Ross of Mull.

32. The marble quarry at Elgol on the Isle of Skye is the home of the famous Skye marble.

Sapphires also occur on Glebe Hill 1.5 km ($\frac{3}{4}$ mile) north-west of the village of Kilchoan on Ardnamurchan, also in the Tertiary lava area. Minute crystals of the same mineral were recorded by Matthew Forster Heddle, the famous Scottish mineralogist, as occurring at Clashnarae Hill, Glen Clova, Aberdeenshire.

Returning to the mainland we find garnets are present in the mica schist to the north and west of Loch Awe, and in fact this gemstone can be traced eastward in a line north of the Highland Boundary Fault, past Glen Shee and Glen Clova, into Angus. Kyanite has been found on the Struan road, between Trinafour and Kinloch Rannoch in the schists, but it occurs reasonably commonly in the rocks further to the north.

Garnets of little distinction can be found near Pitlochry and better specimens occur in the Braes of Balquhidder in Perthshire. Further east we find yet another attractive serpentine amongst the limestone of Glen Tilt.

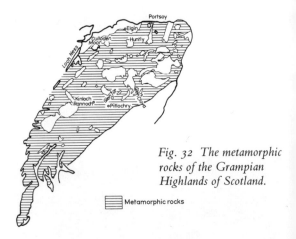

Fig. 32 The metamorphic rocks of the Grampian Highlands of Scotland.

Metamorphic rocks

Travelling to the north we find serpentine, of the type metamorphosed from basalt, in an attractive green and red colour at Portsoy, in Banffshire, with tourmaline and garnet. However, the serpentine ridge extends southwards to Knock Hill out-cropping at several places en route. It also occurs near Huntly and Strathdon. This is the area of Culloden Moor which is the scene of the famous battle and is a locality for sphene.

Turning northwards we find garnet is again common in the schists of Ross-shire with cordierite. Spinel occurs at several localities including Croc Led Beg in Sutherland and in Glenelg in Inverness-shire.

At Bettyhill, on the border of Caithness, we find garnet again in the familiar schist and this brings us to the Orkneys and Shetlands. There is little of interest in Orkney, but mica schist occurs on the Shetland mainland, while at Hillwick blue kyanite, green fluorite, garnet and tourmaline are found. Kyanite also occurs at Vanleep.

Serpentine again appears on Unst, and sphene occurs in gneiss on Burra. Uvarovite, a more unusual green garnet, occurs in a chromite deposit at Baltasound on Fetlar and is said to be the only occurrence of this rare garnet in Britain.

Further south the igneous rocks of the Midland Valley certainly have a metamorphic aureole, but this is not usually exposed. In any case, in this area the abundance of the quartz gemstones such as agate and amethyst has completely over-shadowed the occurrence of other minerals more difficult to find.

It may be pointed out that the small diamonds once credited to a coal seam at Craigman near New Cumnock in Ayrshire were a mineralogical error. The subsequent discrediting of this occurrence has been under-publicized.

England and Wales

Generally speaking England and Wales are too sedimentary-dominated to hold much in the way of metamorphic minerals. For the most part metamorphic rocks are only to be found in Shropshire, Anglesey and Cornwall.

Starting in the north we find that metamorphic rocks are almost absent from the Lake District scene, although they may be represented by Skiddaw Slates which have been modified from shales and mudstones. Here we find galena and sphalerite with fluorite, witherite and baryte, but they are also associated with the adjoining Carboniferous Limestone and are not metamorphic minerals. However garnet occurs in metamorphosed basalt at Shap.

It is interesting to note here the attractive green lakeland slate, which is used locally as an ornamental stone. This rock which began life as Volcanic ash has found great application in ornaments, plaques and jewellery.

Moving southwards we find gneiss, serpentine, schist and quartzite on Anglesey, and gneiss along the Lleyn Peninsula, but minerals are scarce. Glaucophane has been reported in the mica schists on Anglesey, and the serpentine occurs at Parys copper mine with sphalerite, anglesite, galena and chalcopyrite.

33. *Garnet from the Blue Quarry at Shap in Cumbria. The garnet is found in volcanic rocks which were meta-morphosed by the Shap granite. Size 2 mm diameter.*

34. *Lakeland Slate can be made into ornaments and jewellery. These attractive pieces are the work of Ian and Rhona Mathews of Crosby Garrett, Cumbria.*

Red jasper occurs at Aberdaron where it is associated with the phyllites, mica-chlorite schists and gneiss. The increasing effect of metamorphism can be clearly seen in this area of Wales.

If we now travel through Central Wales and across the border into England we find schist, gneiss and quartzite by Primrose Hill, near the Wrekin. Specific mineral sites have not been recorded here but garnet and epidote are features of the schists.

We must now move south and west to Cornwall, stopping off briefly to examine the schists of Start Point, in Devon, where the accessory minerals, tourmaline, epidote, rutile and ilmenite have been recorded. These rocks are believed to be metamorphosed sandstones, shales, siltstones and basaltic lavas.

Fig. 33 The metamorphic rocks of the Lizard, Cornwall.

Nearby on the Lizard Peninsula we find not only serpentine, but gneiss and schist in something of a geological jigsaw. The serpentine has been used extensively for small ornaments, which are a popular buy with tourists, and the same material is utilized by the amateur lapidary fraternity. Not all the serpentine is ideal for ornamental purposes, and it is the Verde Antique for which one should search. Serpentinite, the rock, forms much of the Lizard, but serpentine (mineral serpentine) also occurs, when ideally it is a dark translucent green. Red and black colouring is created by impurities.

Calcite occurs as veins within the serpentine, and copper may also occur as flecks and thin layers. Bastite, tremolite, bronzite (a variety of pyroxene), corderite, chromite, jadeite and the zeolites also occur among the serpentine, but not as collectable minerals.

*35. Kynance Cove on the Lizard Peninsula is situated upon the
metamorphic rock, serpentine.*

The hornblende schists, which form the rock structure to the
north of the serpentine, contain some epidote and grossular
garnet. Olivine has been reported in the Lizard area but to the
best of my knowledge this is unsubstantiated.

Interesting, but of little value to the mineral collector, is the
fact that the Eddystone Reef, situated approximately fourteen
miles to the south of Plymouth, is formed of garnetiferous
gneiss. And so finally we come to Ireland.

Ireland

In Ireland, metamorphic rocks are mainly confined to the
north-west, although there is a significant metamorphic aureole
around some of the larger masses of granite.

Moving out to the west, we find grossular garnet in the
aureole of the Galway granite, and here also we have the
extremely attractive Connemara marble, which is serpentine.
An old reference states that excellent material occurs at the
Ballynahinch quarries. Further north in Mayo we find amethyst
and rose quartz on Achill Island; serpentine near Westport, and
mica schist containing kyanite and garnet near Ennis.

Donegal offers the next major mass of metamorphic rocks and several varieties of garnet can be found throughout the area. Garnet, kyanite, sillimanite, idocrase and staurolite are to be found near Lough Garten; while garnet, andalusite and idocrase occur near Portnoo. Kyanite can be found at Carrowstrasna and hematite occurs near Killybegs, in the same area.

The search for good examples of metamorphic minerals and pegmatites may be a long and arduous one, but there are few feelings to compare with the satisfaction of breaking open the rock to reveal a cavity lined with large and beautiful crystals.

CHAPTER EIGHT

MINERALS AND THE MOVING LANDSCAPE

In the last six chapters we have seen how the rocks of the British Isles were created, and when. We have also seen how minerals have been formed down the ages, and where they can be found in Britain today. But this story, much like a jig-saw, still has one piece missing, and it is a very vital piece.

Despite our recent journey back into geological history, we are still unable to explain certain peculiar phenomena. For instance, we have not explained why agates can be found upon the beaches of Yorkshire, Lincolnshire and Norfolk, when the volcanic rocks in which they are formed are not to be found south of Northumberland. Nor can we explain the presence of amber on these beaches. Amber is a fossil resin from prehistoric trees and is normally found in Poland and East Germany, on the Baltic coast. Another puzzling fact is that pebbles of rhomb-porphyry have been found on the beaches near Scarborough. This rather unusual rock is only found *in situ* in Norway. It does not occur in Britain. To solve these problems we have to delve back into the past yet again and the story I have to unfold is one of erosion and destruction.

The earth's erosive forces are always hard at work and have been so almost since the moment that the earth's first rocks were formed. Their purpose is to level the earth's great mountains and continents until they are obliterated from the scene. If it were not for the earth's mountain-building processes, this would have been accomplished long ago.

As it is, however, when erosion has almost achieved its aim, the earth obligingly creates another set of mountains for erosion to work on. Of course mountains are not created that quickly, they take many millions of years to form, and many millions of years to wear down.

If you should gaze out of your window on a wet and blustery day you will be watching nature's erosive forces hard at work. Water is an erosive force which, given time, will wear away any type of rock you care to name. The wind is also a contributing factor, as it whistles along the valleys and over the hills.

The heat of the sun, the winter frost and snow, all add to nature's destructive power, as does the sea which so effectively erodes our coastline.

Erosion is also responsible, although less dramatically so, for your having to repaint your house, repair guttering or replace roof tiles. When these things happen, your house is suffering from the effects of erosion.

Just what effects do the erosive forces have upon the earth's rocks? You can answer this question yourself by getting into your car, driving into the nearest hilly or mountainous area and taking a look around. You will find that the flanks of many hills have a scree upon them. The scree is composed of rock fragments which have been eroded, mainly by frost, wind and rain, from the hill above. You will see drainage channels on many hillsides, and if you examine them you will see that they contain numerous rock fragments. In very wet weather the rock fragments on the scree, and in the drainage ditches, will be washed into the stream below.

The stream not only carries the fragments along, but it also erodes the rocks over which it passes on its way to join the river. Ultimately, the fragments reach the river, and then the sea, but their passage from mountain to beach may take thousands of years. Obviously the erosive nature of the rivers and streams will be constantly supplementing the debris they already contain.

During a dry spell the river will be low and there will be little movement in the shingle, but in excessively wet weather many of the stones will be swept along at a fairly rapid rate by the turbulent water. This action, too, is erosive. As the rock fragments are transported along they are continually colliding with each other and the rocky bed of the river. Naturally, this causes an abrasion of both the rock fragments and the rock surfaces. The result is that the banks and bed of the stream give up rock fragments to the river, and the existing fragments slowly lose their rough angular shape and begin to take the form of pebbles.

In some instances the true pebble shape is only formed considerably later when the fragment has been shaped on a beach, but if you examine the higher reaches of many rivers and streams you will be amazed at the smoothness of much of the shingle. Of course much of the small material reaches the sea, but is eroded into tiny particles which form sand and gravel.

The sea is probably the earth's single greatest erosive force, as its waves continually break against the rocky cliffs around our shores. The cliffs slowly succumb to the sea's persuasiveness, and fragments of rock join the pebbles on the beach. Eventually, when they have been pushed and pulled along with the shingle countless times, they, too, will become smooth and rounded pebbles.

Rock fragments brought down a river will also receive similar treatment, and will either become pebble shaped, or will wear away, to become just grains of sand. The harder rocks bear up well under the effects of erosion, and as a result many igneous and metamorphic rock pebbles can be expected on the beach. It is the softer sedimentary rocks such as shale, some sandstones and coal which are rapidly worn away. However, much of the amber which occurs as small pebbles on Britain's East Coast is thought to have been preserved by its characteristic lightness.

From the rock collector's point of view, the important feature of the processes of erosion is its characteristic distributive action. If a particularly interesting rock occurs in the hills, when it has been eroded, pebbles of the rock can be found on beaches near the mouth of the nearest river. The same would apply to minerals and other interesting stones.

However, when rock fragments or pebbles arrive on a beach, they have only completed the first stage of a severe obstacle race, and there is more trouble ahead. It doesn't matter which beach you visit, or when, you can be certain of one thing; all the pebbles and shingle on it will be at various stages on a long journey.

Longshore drift

The fact is that beach shingle is on the move, virtually all the time. Every wave that breaks and each resulting backwash are carefully propelling pebbles in one direction along the shore, the direction of movement being decided by the prevailing wind.

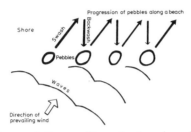

Fig. 34 A diagram illustrating longshore drift.

As you will have realized if you have watched the sea at work, when the wind is blowing off the sea the waves approach the beach from the same direction; they have the wind behind them. The forward motion of the waves moves the pebbles up the beach, in the same direction as that of the wind. When the wave is spent, gravity draws the water and pebbles back down the beach by the quickest route. The next wave breaks and the pebbles are again caught and propelled up the beach in the direction of the wind. The resulting zig-zag motion creates a movement of shingle along a beach as directed by the prevailing wind. On the West Coast the movement of shingle is to the north, on the South Coast the pebbles progress eastwards and on the East Coast, the motion is southwards.

This process, which is called longshore drift, has distributed beach pebbles along large stretches of coast, and goes some way to explaining the occurrence of gemstones, such as agate, on beaches many miles from where they belong. Agate, chalcedony and carnelian are prime examples. They are eroded from hills and cliffs in the north of England and Scotland; they are washed into rivers which carry them to the East Coast, where the sea in its turn distributes them southwards in accordance with the wind.

*Fig. 35   The movement of
shingle around our coast.*

The processes of erosion and longshore drift have distributed semi-precious stones upon many of Britain's beaches. The East Coast has undoubtedly benefited most, but the South and West Coasts have been made more interesting and rewarding from the rock collector's point of view.

There is, however, one of nature's most powerful forces of erosion which we have not yet considered, and in the past this has had a considerable effect, not only on the appearance of Britain, but also upon the distribution of minerals and gemstones over our countryside. The forces to which I refer are the glaciers of the ice age.

The Great Ice Age

The part of geological history known as the Great Ice Age began around two million years ago at a time when the northern hemisphere was undergoing a change of climate. The warm winds from the west no longer blew across our shores; instead they dipped away to the south across Southern Europe and North Africa, and so cold, near arctic, conditions came south to Britain.

Initially, the climatic change was gradual, but before long the heat of the summer was insufficient to melt the winter snows. Large masses of snow began to build up on the high ground of Northern England and Scotland. Eventually, as year by year the snow became deeper, it was transformed into glacier ice. Slowly the ice moved down off the hills and mountains, and began to spread its icy fingers out over the British tundra. Often the ice was many hundreds of feet thick and consequently the glacier completely covered most of the lower hills and many of the mountains in their path.

The general movement of the ice was southwards, until it

arrived at a latitude beyond which the temperature was too warm for it to survive. At this point the forward motion ceased and the ice melted. The glaciers, or ice sheets as the larger masses are called, moved southwards on no fewer than four occasions, each being called a glaciation. Between the glaciations were interglacial periods of warmer weather up to 15,000 years in duration. It is generally considered that we are living in just such an interglacial period today.

The movement of thousands of tons of ice is no easy matter and the effects of this process can still be seen on the British landscape. Many of our valleys were lengthened and broadened by the passage of large masses of ice, the peaks of our mountains were sharpened, while the lesser hills were almost totally obliterated from the scene. There is no doubt that the glaciers were largely responsible for creating the scenery we enjoy in Britain today. And talking of scenery it was only at the end of the last glaciation some 10,000 years ago, that the rock structure around Britain slowly subsided allowing water to flood into what we now call the English Channel.

When the large masses of glacier ice flowed over the hills, they smoothed the rock surfaces and removed a countless number of rock fragments of all sizes and varieties. This rock debris was carried along southwards beneath the ice until it melted, when the rock debris was abandoned exactly where it stood. Frequently the rock fragments would have travelled long distances southwards with the ice and now lie abandoned in countryside far removed from the hills in which they were created. The rock debris, which is now called boulder clay, covers much of lowland Britain, but as the ice never advanced to the south of a line from the River Severn to the Thames, Southern England is free from these glacial remains.

Bearing in mind that the contents of the boulder clay are representatives of the rocks over which the ice passed, it stands to reason that a wide range of different types of rock are contained within it. When the glaciers passed over areas where gemstones occurred, then these too were carried southwards. Consequently, in the Midlands and the North of England, gemstones can be found which were originally created many miles away to the north in Scotland.

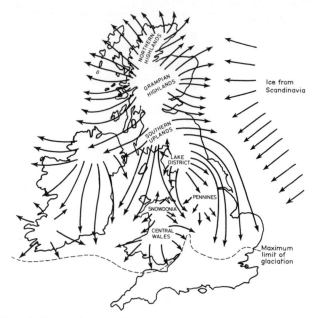

*Fig. 36 A map showing the direction of ice movement from the high
ground in the British Isles at the height of the Ice Age.*

On the East and West Coasts, there are areas where the
boulder clay forms cliffs, and here the tide washes the rock
fragments, including gemstones, out onto the beach for
longshore drift to distribute. This has resulted in several areas of
coast being comparatively rich in gemstones.

In addition to glacial deposits containing British rock
fragments, the scene is further complicated by the presence of
boulder clay which originated in Norway. This debris was
brought here by ice which traversed what is now the North Sea.
This factor explains the presence of rhomb porphyry, a
Scandinavian rock, on the beaches of Yorkshire.

The coast is not the only area affected by glacial deposits for
they cover most of the countryside, except the high ground,
from which they have been eroded. The presence of fluvioglacial deposits in various areas of the country may also interest
the collector. As the ice melted, large lakes were formed by
rapidly flowing rivers, which emerged from under the ice. The

melt waters carried rock debris out into the lakes where it accumulated. On occasions, the lakes overspilled their banks and the rock debris was distributed over the countryside. It is the debris from the beds of the rivers and lakes which is worked under the name fluvioglacial deposits today. Not surprisingly, a wide variety of rocks, minerals and gemstones may be found in these deposits.

36. Glacial deposits in the form of boulder clay occur as cliffs on many parts of our coast. Being soft the clay is easily eroded by the sea. This photograph illustrates erosion in action.

Minerals on Britain's beaches

The processes of erosion which have moved rocks and minerals around Britain have usually acted on a broad scale. Consequently if a gemstone, which has been moved by such action, is found in one particular spot, then it will probably occur throughout the surrounding area. Of course, only hard stones will have survived the erosive processes, all the softer materials having been worn away. Quartz is the only common hard mineral and for the most part, it is the gemstone varieties of this mineral that have been distributed to the collector's advantage.

Unfortunately, Scotland has not fared well at the hands of erosion. Many glaciers started from the Scottish Mountains and moved southwards into England carrying what gemstones were present away from the north. The coastline of Scotland is so irregular that longshore drift has had only a limited effect on the distribution of interesting gemstones.

If we start in the far north of Scotland on the East Coast at Helmsdale, we find that erosion has provided us with yellow jasper, chalcedony, fossil wood and fossil coral. Specimens of each can be found on the beach at Port Navidale, but a wide variety of Jurassic fossils occur on the coast here. Moving southwards to Golspie in Sutherland, we find amethyst, smoky quartz and rock crystal among the shingle where they have arrived after being carried down a small burn to the north. Common chalcedony, carnelian and occasionally agate occur in association with flint on the same beach.

37. The beach at Helmsdale is famous for the wide range of fossils it contains.

Moving out along the south bank of the Moray Firth we find serpentine on the beach at Portsoy where it has been eroded from the nearby cliffs. Being soft in nature, the serpentine has not survived to be found on other beaches in the area. A rather unusual occurrence on certain beaches on the Moray Firth is the presence of small agate pebbles. It is difficult to account for the presence of agate here but it is virtually certain that they have been transported to the area by the forces of erosion.

The beaches become more interesting as we progress southwards into Aberdeenshire and by the time we have reached Montrose in Angus, they have become rich in mineralogical delights. Jasper, in a wide variety of colours, is present on the vast majority of beaches while agate, chalcedony and amethyst are also added to the beach by the erosion of the lava cliffs at St Cyrus and Montrose. Agate, together with chalcedony, is a common find on most beaches from Lunan Bay southwards to St Andrews in Fife, thanks to the effect of longshore drift. Also near St Andrews, amber occurs on the beaches near the mouth of the River Eden.

The beach near Dunglass in East Lothian is a site for agate and jasper, the former in finely banded and attractively coloured specimens. The occasional specimen of both these gemstones may be found on beaches to the south.

Crossing the border into England we find the quantity of agate on the beach increasing as the Rivers Tweed, Aln and Coquet add more and more specimens to the beaches. The rivers rise in the Cheviot Hills and it is here that the agate originates. The beaches of Holy Island also yield agate together with pyrite. Glacial deposits surround the Cheviot Hills and contain agate, tourmaline and chalcedony.

38. The boulder clay cliffs at Carnelian Bay yield many beautiful gemstones which may be found amongst the shingle.

Passing southwards into Yorkshire we leave the industrial coastline of Durham behind and find a string of excellent gemstone beaches along the length of the Yorkshire coast. Agate and chalcedony are common on many of the beaches but pride of place here goes to the pretty orange carnelian which occurs on several beaches including Carnelian Bay and Robin Hood's Bay. Due to glacial action, jet is quite a common find on many beaches in the Whitby area. Amber is much sought after on the beaches south of Bridlington, but I have every reason to believe that this attractive material occurs quite commonly further north.

39. Agate pebbles from the east coast beaches of England. Size (centre specimen) 45 mm. diameter.

The beaches of Norfolk offer interesting specimens of amber and agate but by now the effect of longshore drift is decreasing and we are coming to the most southerly extent of the glacial deposits. As we turn the corner on to the Kent coast, we find only a trace of the agate and chalcedony which dominated the beaches of Norfolk and Yorkshire, and the absence of glacial deposits in the south has made for less interesting beaches. Only longshore drift has any effect on the distribution and content of the shingle on the South Coast and the overall movement of shingle is west to east.

Marcasite from the chalk cliffs of Kent occurs widely upon beaches in the east and the occasional specimen of agate has been traced on the beach at Hastings and at Sandown on the Isle of Wight. Flint dominates the scene at Chesil Beach but generally speaking there is little else of interest in this area. Further to the west the beaches of Charmouth are famous for the fossils they contain, many of which are preserved in pyrite. Small misshapen lumps of the same material also occur in the shingle and are usually found around the base of the larger boulders on the beach.

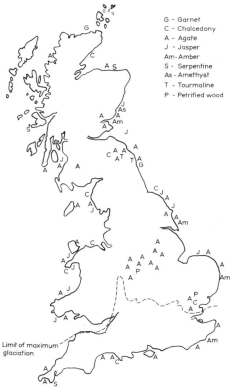

G - Garnet
C - Chalcedony
A - Agate
J - Jasper
Am - Amber
S - Serpentine
As - Amethyst
T - Tourmaline
P - Petrified wood

Limit of maximum glaciation

Fig. 37 A map of gemstone and mineral sites which have been created by the processes of erosion.

Rock crystal, chalcedony and agate are found in association with chert beds which exist in the cliffs to the west of Lyme Regis. Specimens of these gemstones together with hollow, crystal-lined 'potato stones' may be found on many beaches between Lyme Regis and Budleigh Salterton.

The beaches of Cornwall are renowned for the gemstones they contain. Agate pebbles are particularly abundant and can be found on most beaches but especially those in Mount's Bay. St Michael's Mount is reputedly the home of many gemstones but unfortunately collecting is not allowed. However, pebbles of amethyst have been found on the beach at Marazion and these probably originated on the Mount.

Rounding Land's End and turning to the north we find agate on the beaches near St Ives and Perranporth. Quartz crystals occur in veins and cavities in the headland at Tintagel. Jasper returns to the beaches as we cross North Devon while agate, jasper and crystal-lined 'potato stones' are known on the beaches between Clevedon and Portishead near Bristol.

The south coast of Wales is heavily industrialized, although the occasional specimen of agate and jasper may be found on the more attractive beaches. The presence of agate on these beaches is primarily due to the glacial deposits which can now be seen forming the cliffs as we move to the west. The beaches of The Gower offer an interesting range of pebbles but it is not until we have passed Tenby that semi-precious stones become evident. Vein agate occurs as pebbles on the beaches west of Manorbier along with carnelian and jasper. This is the most productive area for gemstones on the Welsh coast but specimens of the same materials occur on the beaches of Cardigan Bay. Despite the presence of volcanic rocks in the area these gemstones are the product of the glacial deposits and are eroded out of boulder clay by the sea.

The Lleyn Peninsula yields the occasional specimen of agate, but jasper is more common, occurring in quantity at Aberdaron where it has even been incorporated into the promenade. The jasper may contain veins of agate but such specimens are mainly confined to the north coast of the peninsula where carnelian may also be found. Hornstone occurs on the Menai Straits and chalcedony and agate occur on beaches on Anglesey. The Flintshire coast yields jasper and carnelian.

Leaving Wales and proceeding northwards, we find that the industrial scenery of Merseyside is prominent and is followed by the holiday resorts of Blackpool and Morecambe. Fluvioglacial deposits have been worked near Grange-over-Sands and contain the usual quota of chalcedony gemstones. Jasper, agate, carnelian and some grey chalcedony can be found on the coast of Cumbria. Fleswick Bay at St Bee's Head is a good place to search for specimens.

40. Beaches frequently offer a wide range of interesting pebbles and semi-precious stones. The beach illustrated is on the Lleyn Peninsula, North Wales.

Entering Southern Scotland, jasper and rock crystal occur on the Kirkcudbright coast, and the occasional specimen of amethyst may be found by Wigtown Bay. North of Stranraer the beaches become increasingly rich in agate, chalcedony, amethyst and smoky quartz as we approach the city of Ayr. The Heads of Ayr are composed of andesite, a volcanic rock of Old Red Sandstone Age, and agates are a common find. The agates find their way on to the beach by the erosion of the nearby cliffs. Culzean Castle, the property of the National Trust for Scotland, stands on top of cliffs which also contain agates and these too are added to the beach. Specimens of agate and associated gemstones may be found on many beaches north of Ayr along the Firth of Clyde.

The effect of longshore drift is to move pebbles northwards along the West Coast, but once past the Firth of Clyde the coast becomes rugged and the effects of this process are minimized if not totally eliminated. Consequently, the collector must step out on to the beaches, uncertain as to what they may contain, but he may be in for many a nice surprise.

Beaches on the Isle of Arran yield agate and chalcedony and both these gemstones occur on the Mull of Kintyre. All the beaches south of Campbeltown yield carnelian and agate while Machrihanish Bay is a site for chalcedony and beryl.

Agate, chalcedony, amethyst and smoky quartz occur on many beaches in the south and west of the Isle of Mull, and on Skye. Jasper occurs on several of the more exposed beaches on the coast of Ross-shire and may be found with pieces of small red agate at Ardmair Bay near Ullapool. The west coast beaches of Sutherland are rather few and far between, but agate has been reported two kilometres to the south of Cape Wrath.

The north coast of Scotland has many beautiful beaches which are, however, essentially devoid of gemstones. The only exceptions to this are at Tongue, where nice pieces of amazonite may be found, and at Bettyhill where garnet may be dug out of the shingle. Garnets may also be found among the river gravel up Strath Naver.

The beaches of Caithness are rather more interesting but lacking in gemstones. Flint in a range of colours is quite common here as is a brown and white flecked puddingstone. However, pride of place such as it is, goes to an attractive black limestone which, being hard, is useful to a lapidary. Fluvioglacial deposits are worked at several localities in Caithness but are unrewarding from the collector's point of view.

Leaving the coast behind, the presence of glacial deposits has to be assumed, for rarely are they seen. However, wherever interesting gemstones occur in the bed rock, the surrounding boulder clay is sure to contain them. In some areas of Scotland where agate is plentiful, it is possible to predict locations at which agate may be found in boulder clay. Detective work of this type may be very rewarding.

The fluvioglacial deposits of East Fife are well known for the beautiful agates they contain, and similar deposits in Southern

Scotland are also productive. Gravel pits near Doncaster in Yorkshire, Lichfield in Staffordshire and Bromsgrove in Worcestershire also yield worthwhile specimens. Agate has also been found, and is remarkably common, in fields between Worksop and Retford in Nottinghamshire. Glacial action in association with the River Trent is responsible for this concentration of gemstones.

41. Gravel pits working fluvioglacial deposits often have gemstones among the pebbles. This gravel pit is near Wormit in Fife and contains agate and chalcedony pebbles.

The southernmost extent of the glacial deposits follow a line from the River Severn to the Thames; consequently the South of England lacks the interest that the ice age has created in the rest of Britain. However, fluvioglacial deposits south of this line in Essex contain agate and chalcedony. These deposits were undoubtedly created by melt waters from the ice which moved southwards.

We have now concluded our journey around Britain's rock and mineral sites. Our next and final task is to consider the different techniques we may use to identify minerals.

CHAPTER NINE

IDENTIFYING MINERALS AND GEMSTONES

Identifying rocks is not usually difficult and can be achieved quite readily with a suitable geological map. Minerals however are more of a problem and I hope the following methods of identification and tables will be helpful.

Hardness

MOHS' SCALE OF HARDNESS		
No. 1	talc	
No. 2	gypsum	$2\frac{1}{2}$—finger nail
No. 3	calcite	
No. 4	fluorite	4—copper coin
No. 5	apatite	$5\frac{1}{2}$—penknife blade
No. 6	feldspar	$6\frac{1}{2}$—steel file
No. 7	quartz	
No. 8	topaz	
No. 9	corundum	
No. 10	diamond	

The hardness of a mineral or gemstone offers a vital clue to its identification. Consider quartz as an example. Quartz at 7 on Mohs' Scale will scratch any of the minerals below it, but is vulnerable to being scratched by topaz, corundum or diamond, the minerals above it on the scale. Diamond will scratch all the minerals, while talc can be scratched by them all.

The collector can use a variety of common objects to pinpoint minerals on the scale, Talc and gypsum can be scratched by the finger nail. Calcite can be scratched by a copper coin while fluorspar and apatite may be defaced by use of a steel file. Quartz will scratch the steel and, considering the rarity of topaz, corundum and diamond, the collector in Britain has little need to worry about minerals harder than 7. It is not advisable to employ a diamond of jewellery quality in an attempt to determine the hardness of other minerals.

Hardness is a useful guide, for it can be employed on the site, and there are several other equally helpful tests, which can save you carrying home a large lump of stone in the belief that it is something it isn't.

Crystal form

Minerals are either amorphous or crystalline, the former having no regular arrangement of their component atoms. Fortunately most minerals are crystalline, the orderly arrangement of their internal structure giving rise to a repeatable crystal form. Crystal form is therefore a relatively simple way of identifying a mineral. Often the crystals you will find will be very small, but the use of a reasonable quality hand lens will aid identification.

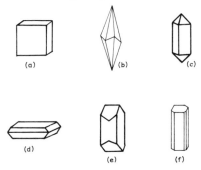

Fig. 38 Examples of crystals in the six crystal systems. (a) a cubic crystal of fluorite; (b) a hexagonal crystal of calcite; (c) a tetragonal crystal of zircon; (d) an orthorhombic crystal of baryte; (e) a monoclinic crystal of orthoclase feldspar; (f) a triclinic crystal of kyanite.

There are six crystal systems which the minerals can adopt, but there are many crystal forms in each system.

Streak

A streak test is achieved when a mineral is scraped across an unglazed piece of porcelain. The back of a porcelain tile is quite adequate. Each mineral scraped will leave a streak, which is not necessarily the colour of the mineral.

Chalcopyrite (copper pyrite) is a good example. It appears brass yellow in the hand but gives a green/black streak. Another example is biotite (mica). This gives a white streak although in colour it is black/brown.

A small piece of tile will slip easily into a pocket and certainly helps ease the problem of identification.

Fracture

The way a mineral fractures can also give clues to its identity.

42. Flint (left) showing its typical conchoidal fracture. Calcite (right) exhibiting its rhombohedral cleavage. Size: flint 35 × 40 mm, calcite 40 × 55 mm.

Perhaps the best-known fracture is that of quartz (and also glass). This is known as a conchoidal fracture; but several other types are recognized including brittle, even and uneven.

43. Many minerals do not exhibit their crystal forms but may often adopt a characteristic appearance. The specimen illustrated is of chalcedony displaying its common botryoidal (bunch of grapes) form. This specimen is from Tayport, Fife. Size 75 × 80 mm.

Transparency and lustre

This is another excellent test which can be carried out simply by looking at the specimen. Some minerals are transparent, others are translucent, and of course there are many opaque minerals. Many metallic minerals have a metallic lustre, while calcite has a vitreous lustre. Quartz, on the other hand, has a glassy lustre, while diamond has an adamantine lustre.

Lustre, of course, is the way in which the surface of a mineral reflects the light. Other terms used to define lustre are pearly, silky, fatty and resinous.

Cleavage

Cleavage is the characteristic some minerals have of splitting along one or more planes related to their internal structure. Some minerals, of course, have no planes of cleavage, while others may have several.

Mica is a good example, splitting as it does into thin flakes. Calcite, on the other hand, cleaves into well-defined and easily identifiable rhombohedrons. The only danger is that the cleavage plane can be confused with a crystal surface. Quartz for example has crystal surfaces, but does not cleave.

Colour

The colour of a mineral specimen is perhaps the first thing the collector notices, and as first impressions are often difficult to erase from one's mind, it is essential that the importance of colour as an identifying factor is fully appreciated.

In fact, colour is very misleading. A specimen which has been recently exposed to the atmosphere will not have suffered the weathering which so readily disguises many specimens. However, all specimens are likely to have been coated by other minerals during their formation, which may introduce a false colour.

Of course, many minerals occur in a variety of colours and shades, depending upon the nature of the occurrence.

Weight

The weight of a mineral specimen is perhaps the crudest of the simple methods of identification. It stands to reason that only for extremely light or heavy materials will it offer any clue, for the vast majority of minerals are similar in weight.

Galena (lead sulphide) along with baryte (barium sulphate), also called 'heavy spar', can be picked out fairly easily by their excessive weight; while amber is readily identifiable due to being very light.

Inevitably there are many more methods of identifying minerals. Specific gravity, which is the weight of the mineral in air, divided by its weight in water, offers quite a reasonable guide, but the accurate balance required is not available to many collectors.

The behaviour of a mineral when placed in a blowpipe flame also offers clues, but again is not the most simple test to be carried out in the home.

Of course the conclusive test is that performed in a laboratory, where chemicals are employed in determining the character of the mineral; but again this facility is available to very few.

There are other complications. Many mineral specimens occur together, and consequently you can find one sample with three or four minerals attached. This makes the task of identification very difficult, especially as some minerals may be present as an encrustation or even as an inclusion in a crystal. This is all part of the game.

In practice some minerals, like calcite or quartz, are a good deal more common than others, and identifying them soon becomes second nature. There is however one other vital piece of information which can considerably reduce the number of possibilities the collector is faced with when identifying a mineral. This factor is the rock/mineral relationship. Every type of rock has certain minerals which are to be expected in association with it. In limestone, for example, calcite is a certain find, and also dolomite or aragonite; while in granite one might find quartz or mica. Rock/mineral associations are very important and an understanding of them can save many fruitless hours spent sifting through identification tables.

Perhaps, having said this, a final word of caution. Always be ready for the unexpected. After all, nature has created many wonderful minerals and she is always capable of producing a surprise or two, especially when you're least expecting it.

CHAPTER TEN

MINERAL COLLECTOR'S GUIDE

By now it will have become apparent that minerals occur widely throughout the British Isles. You may find them on mountain sides, in quarries, on mine dumps, along the sea-shore and even in fields on agricultural land. It follows that the collecting techniques and the equipment required to collect minerals at these locations will differ, consequently I hope the following guide will prove useful.

44. Rock collecting equipment. A lump hammer and cold chisel may be used to extract mineral specimens from rock crevices, while a rock pick may also be useful. Safety glasses are, of course, essential. Newspaper is suitable for wrapping delicate specimens. The collector of pebbles may find a polythene bag sufficient, although a haversack may be necessary for heavier pieces.

Collecting equipment

Hammer	A wide range of hammers are available depending upon the purpose for which you require them. A geologist's rock pick is useful for breaking off rock specimens, but a 2 lb lump hammer is more valuable when using a cold chisel.
Cold chisel	A selection of alloy steel chisels will prove useful for breaking rocks.
Safety glasses	Breaking rocks can be accompanied by flying splinters, consequently I consider safety glasses to be essential.
Haversack and wrapping materials	Newspaper is ideal for protecting delicate specimens and a haversack is ideal for carrying them home in. The pebble collector can manage with a plastic bag.
Geological Maps	Geological Maps of the 'drift' variety are ideal for the collector. The maps show where solid rock is exposed and also indicate the presence of glacial deposits. The 'solid' type of map ignores glacial deposits and alluvium.
Ordnance Survey maps	An O.S. map of the same scale as the Geological Map is a great help in finding your way around.

Possible hazards

Mineral collecting can be a perfectly safe pastime providing one obeys the simple rules:

1. Never enter private property without permission. Whether a law of trespass exists or not, removing minerals is illegal. Always ask permission no matter how difficult it may be to find the owner, and always accept his or her decision.

2. In mining areas beware of old mine shafts. Many of these exist and are nothing more than dangerous holes in the ground.

3. When searching in quarries tread carefully and avoid recently blasted rock which may be unstable. Neither should the collector work under overhangs.
4. Always note the time of high tide especially when searching beaches backed by tall cliffs.
5. In the country, follow the country code.
6. Never take more specimens than you need, always leave some for the next collector.

Polishing stones

Many of the harder minerals you may collect can be polished and manufactured into jewellery. Lapidary, which is the name for polishing stones, is a rapidly growing hobby and many collectors specialize in collecting stones suitable for this purpose.

Generally speaking minerals with a hardness above 6 on Mohs' Scale of Hardness are ideal for polishing although there are exceptions. Both jet and Blue John are soft materials which can be polished although the latter stone is difficult due to its coarsely crystalline character. The different varieties of quartz are most suitable polishing material, and in Britain gemstones such as agate, chalcedony and jasper are reasonably abundant.

Lapidary techniques vary depending upon whether you require a curved surface or a flat surface to be polished. Both processes require equipment which can be obtained from lapidary dealers, there being many shops throughout the country. Most lapidary techniques require some degree of skill but the exception to this is the tumble polishing process. A tumble polishing machine is ideal for polishing pebbles, the process taking one month. No skill is required and providing the simple instructions are followed polished pebbles will be yours at the end of the process. Tumble polishing machines can be obtained cheaply or assembled by the 'do it yourself' enthusiast for little more than the cost of a motor.

In order to distinguish between British minerals which are suitable for polishing and those that are not, minerals which occur in a polishable quality are accompanied by the following symbol ★ in the Mineral Catalogue.

A LIST OF MINERAL LOCALITIES IN ENGLAND, WALES AND SCOTLAND

Each locality is accompanied by the appropriate Ordnance Survey Sheet number in brackets followed by a six-figure grid reference.

The numbers listed after symbol (M) relate to the minerals which commonly occur at the locality. The numbers relate to minerals listed in the Mineral Catalogue.

A

Aberdaron O.S. Sheet (123) 173264 (M) 111, 113
Abergairn O.S. Sheet (44) 357973 (M) 6, 18, 34, 62
Achanarras O.S. Sheet (12) 150545 (M) 6, 8, 27, 34, 62, 99
Achnasheen O.S. Sheet (25) 158585 (M) 108
Agate Knowe O.S. Sheet (54) 253299 (M) 26, 42, 57, 68, 102, 111
Aldborough (Yorkshire) O.S. Sheet (107) 242386 (M) 70
Aldeburgh (Suffolk) O.S. Sheet (156) 466565 (M) 70
Alderley Edge O.S. Sheet (118) 843785 (M) 80, 82, 92
Allt Dearg O.S. Sheet (20) 260800 (M) 67, 116
Aln, R. O.S. Sheet (81) 990110 (M) 26, 42, 111
Anglesey O.S. Sheet (114) (M) 26, 42, 95, 111
Arbor Low O.S. Sheet (119) 162633 (M) 8
Ardmair Bay O.S. Sheet (19) 110983 (M) 42, 111, 113
Ardnamurchan O.S. Sheet (47) (M) 23, 98
Armadale O.S. Sheet (32) 638040 (M) 108
Assynt O.S. Sheet (15) 315202 (M) brucite marble
Auchmithie O.S. Sheet (54) 680443 (M) 113
Avon, R. O.S. Sheet (36) 164167 (M) 26, 27, 68, 108

Castleton O.S. Sheet (119) 151830 (M) 62
Castletown O.S. Sheet (12) 196430 (M) 99
Cavedale O.S. Sheet (119) 151827 (M) 6, 8, 18, 42
Charmouth O.S. Sheet (193) 366936 (M) 6, 26, 42, 76, 111
Cheviot Hills O.S. Sheet (80) (M) 6, 27, 42, 45, 57, 68, 82, 106, 111,
    113, 116
Cleator Moor O.S. Sheet (89) 020150 (M) 68
Clevedon O.S. Sheet (172) 411719 (M) 102, 111, 113
Cleveland O.S. Sheet (94) 670007 (M) 61
Cligga Mine O.S. Sheet (204) 739537 (M) 18, 28, 40, 43, 51, 56, 71, 73,
    104
Colbost O.S. Sheet (23) 380318 (M) 115
Colchester O.S. Sheet (168) 949236 (M) 26, 42, 78, 102, 111, 113
Coll O.S. Sheet (46) (M) 8
Coombe Martin O.S. Sheet (180) 590460 (M) 34, 36, 48, 62, 77, 82
Coquet, R. O.S. Sheet (80) 900062 (M) 26, 42, 78, 102, 111, 113
Corstorphine Hill O.S. Sheet (66) 744205 (M) 21, 102
Craiglockhart Qy O.S. Sheet (66) 232705 (M) 102
Criffell O.S. Sheet (83) 957619 (M) 106
Croscombe O.S. Sheet (183) 591444 (M) 33
Cuillins O.S. Sheet (32) 450220 (M) 46, 52, 86, 97
Culloden O.S. Sheet (27) 735455 (M) 75
Culzean O.S. Sheet (70) 230100 (M) 6, 26, 42, 57, 102, 111, 113

D
Dirtlow Rake O.S. Sheet (119) 150819 (M) 6, 8, 18, 34
Dover O.S. Sheet (179) 320412 (M) 77
Dulcote Qy O.S. Sheet (182) 570442 (M) 6, 26, 27, 34, 49, 60, 68, 102,
    111, 113
Dunglass O.S. Sheet (67) 764724 (M) 42, 111, 113
Dunrobin Glen O.S. Sheet (17) 820029 (M) 26, 68, 102
Dunure O.S. Sheet (70) 254160 (M) 6, 26, 68, 102, 112, 113, 114
Dunvegan O.S. Sheet (23) 254476 (M) 42, 100, 111

E
East Harp Tree O. S. Sheet (182) 567556 (M) 33
Ecton Hill O.S. Sheet (118) 100580 (M) 26, 42, 47, 73, 82, 92
Egremont O.S. Sheet (89) 010110 (M) 6, 8, 13, 14, 18, 26, 55, 57, 68,
    106
Elgin O.S. Sheet (28) 188629 (M) 18
Elie Ness O.S. Sheet (59) 494000 (M) 67, 108
Ennerdale O.S. Sheet (89) 100130 (M) 67, 75

F

Fair Isle O.S. Sheet (4) (M) 82
Ferryden O.S. Sheet (54) 715566 (M) 6, 27, 42, 57, 102, 111, 113, 114, 115
Firth of Tay O.S. Sheet (54) 358248 (M) 6, 23, 26, 42, 57, 78, 102, 111, 113
Fleswick Bay O.S. Sheet (89) 946133 (M) 42, 78, 111, 113
Flintshire Coast O.S. Sheet (116) 200780 (M) 78, 111, 113
Florence Mine O.S. Sheet (89) 019102 (M) 6, 11, 13, 18, 26, 55, 106
Folkestone O.S. Sheet (179) 230360 (M) 77
Friden O.S. Sheet (119) 170605 (M) 6, 8, 24, 26, 42, 57, 111

G

Glebe Hill O.S. Sheet (47) 480646 (M) 98
Glebe Mine O.S. Sheet (119) 219775 (M) 24
Glen Clova O.S. Sheet (44) 330730 (M) 1, 41, 98
Glenelg O.S. Sheet (33) 815194 (M) 46, 97
Glen Farg O.S. Sheet (58) 162131 (M) 6, 26, 42, 57, 78, 102, 111
Glengaber Burn O.S. Sheet (71) 850140 (M) 71
Glen Muick O.S. Sheet (44) 320886 (M) 18
Glen Wigle O.S. Sheet (68) 694168 (M) 102
Goatfell O.S. Sheet (69) 990415 (M) 28, 68, 87, 96
Golspie O.S. Sheet (21) 830998 (M) 26, 42, 68, 78, 102, 111
Gortally O.S. Sheet (26) 490310 (M) 94
Guardbridge O.S. Sheet (59) 450190 (M) 70
Gunheath Qy O.S. Sheet (200) 006582 (M)

H

Habberley O.S. Sheet (126) 399036 (M) 8, 35, 82
Halkirk O.S. Sheet (12) 130595 (M) 6, 26, 27, 34, 62
Halkyn Mountain O.S. Sheet (117) 203706 (M) 8, 18, 34, 36, 62
Hastings O.S. Sheet (199) 820093 (M) 42, 111
Heads of Ayr O.S. Sheet (70) 284188 (M) 6, 26, 42, 57, 68, 102, 111, 113, 114, 115
Heights Qy O.S. Sheet (92) 925387 (M) 6, 18, 26, 34
Helmsdale O.S. Sheet (17) 030154 (M) 6, 18, 113
Hensbarrow O.S. Sheet (200) 998576 (M) 16, 58, 68, 93, 102
Hillswick O.S. Sheet (3) 282771 (M) 18, 94, 108, 116
Holy Island O.S. Sheet (75) 110435 (M) 42, 76, 111, 113

I

Inverbervie O.S. Sheet (45) 830725 (M) 42, 111, 113
Iona O.S. Sheet (48) 270240 (M) 111, 113, Iona marble

J
Jedburgh O.S. Sheet (74) 650205 (M) 26, 102, 111

K
Kildonan O.S. Sheet (17) 912210 (M) 54, 71, 108
Killelan Hill O.S. Sheet (68) 685155 (M) 111, 113
Kilpatrick Hills O.S. Sheet (64) 465765 (M) 23, 28, 86
Kilsleven Mine O.S. Sheet (60) 415673 (M) 73
Kings Seat O.S. Sheet (53) 230330 (M) 26, 57, 68, 102, 111
Kinnoul Hill O.S. Sheet (58) 137228 (M) 26, 42, 102, 111
Kit Hill O.S. Sheet (201) 375713 (M) 51, 56, 116
Knipe, The O.S. Sheet (71) 658103 (M) 6, 27, 32
Knocknairling Hill O.S. Sheet (77) 620765 (M) 116

L
Leadhills O.S. Sheet (71) 886150 (M) 6, 8, 13, 18, 26, 27, 31, 34, 47, 60,
    62, 73, 76, 80, 81, 82, 83, 105, 106
Lizard, The O.S. Sheet (204) 695115 (M) 39, 63, 66, 69, 87, 89, 90, 94,
    108, 109, 110
Llandrindod O.S. Sheet (161) 060614 (M) 6, 26, 75, 111
Lleyn Peninsula O.S. Sheet (123) (M) 42, 111, 113
Loch Awe O.S. Sheet (55) 980130 (M) 108
Loch Doon O.S. Sheet (77) 490990 (M) 106
Loch Fyne O.S. Sheet (55) 985970 (M) 18, 82
Loe Bar O.S. Sheet (203) 644240 (M) 111, 113
Lomond Hills O.S. Sheet (59) 060240 (M) 26, 42, 102, 111
Lossiemouth O.S. Sheet (28) 237705 (M) 34
Lunan Bay O.S. Sheet (54) 690510 (M) 6, 26, 42, 68, 102, 111, 113, 114
Lyme Regis O.S. Sheet (193) 341921 (M) 6, 26, 42, 76, 111, 113

M
Machrihanish O.S. Sheet (68) 650230 (M) 42
Magpie Mine O.S. Sheet (119) 173682 (M) 6, 8, 18, 34, 62, 103
Marazion O.S. Sheet (203) 517307 (M) 79, 102, 111, 112
Marlbrook Qy O.S. Sheet (139) 985750 (M) 27, 78, 102, 111, 113
Masson Hill O.S. Sheet (119) 286586 (M) 6, 8, 14, 18, 26, 34, 62, 103
Meldon Qy O.S. Sheet (191) 568920 (M) 24, 26, 43, 65, 68, 105, 108
Melsetter O.S. Sheet (7) 270894 (M) 42
Mendip Hills O.S. Sheet (165–6) (M) 6, 34, 57, 60, 102, 111, 113
Millclose Mine O.S. Sheet (119) 255615 (M) 6, 8, 18, 34, 76, 77
Millers Dale O.S. Sheet (119) 152732 (M) 6, 26, 42, 102, 111
Milton O.S. Sheet (26) 495306 (M) 46, 67

Minerva O.S. Sheet (117) 270518 (M) 8, 18, 34, 36, 62, 73
Mogshaw Rake O.S. Sheet (119) 184678 (M) 6, 8, 18, 26, 34, 42, 111
Montrose O.S. Sheet (54) 715574 (M) 6, 26, 42, 57, 102, 111, 113, 114, 115
Mountfield O.S. Sheet (199) 742203 (M) 2, 7

N

Netherfield O.S. Sheet (129) 622408 (M) 111, 113
New Cumnock O.S. Sheet (71) 620133 (M) 29, 32, 44
Normans Law O.S. Sheet (59) 305203 (M) 6, 26, 42, 45, 57, 68, 78, 102, 111, 113

O

Odin Mine O.S. Sheet (119) 134835 (M) 6, 8, 18, 34

P

Pary's Copper Mine O.S. Sheet (114) 440902 (M) 34, 37, 62, 73
Path of Condie O.S. Sheet (58) 074117 (M) 6, 26, 42, 57, 68, 102, 111
Penarth O.S. Sheet (171) 189710 (M) 2
Perranporth O.S. Sheet (200) 755540 (M) 111
Pitlochry O.S. Sheet (53) 940582 (M) 108
Point of Ayr O.S. Sheet (59) 466050 (M) 42, 111, 113
Pole Hill O.S. Sheet (58) 196261 (M) 26, 42, 111
Portishead O.S. Sheet (172) 465765 (M) 111, 113
Port Navidale O.S. Sheet (17) 040160 (M) 6, 113
Portsoy O.S. Sheet (29) 590662 (M) 108, 116, Portsoy marble
Priestlaw O.S. Sheet (67) 651624 (M) 8, 73, 81
Pumpsaint O.S. Sheet (140) 665404 (M) 71

R

Reay O.S. Sheet (11) 960647 (M) 79, 106
Retford O.S. Sheet (120) 700860 (M) 42, 111, 113
Riber Mine O.S. Sheet (119) 299587 (M) 47
Robin Hood's Bay O.S. Sheet (94) 956040 (M) 78, 102, 111, 113, 114
Roche Rock O.S. Sheet (200) 987600 (M) 27, 58
Roughton Gill O.S. Sheet (82) 302345 (M) 80, 82
Rowbarrow O.S. Sheet (182) 454583 (M) 83
Rubislaw Qy O.S. Sheet (38) 911055 (M) 108, 116
Rutland Mine O.S. Sheet (119) 286580 (M) 82, 92

S

St Day O.S. Sheet (204) 734425 (M) 18, 40, 46, 62, 76, 113

St Ives O.S. Sheet (203) 520400 (M) 11, 28, 40, 43, 56, 57, 58, 76, 84, 111

St Just O.S. Sheet (203) 310370 (M) 18, 38, 49, 56, 91, 102, 104, 106, 107

Sandown O.S. Sheet (196) 600840 (M) 111

Sandwich Bay O.S. Sheet (4) 435235 (M) 18, 82

Scobul O.S. Sheet (48) 465270 (M) 26, 42, 98, 102, 111

Scoor O.S. Sheet (48) 417191 (M) 23, 26, 27, 42, 78, 86, 102, 111

Scurdie Ness O.S. Sheet (54) 734568 (M) 6, 26, 68, 102, 111

Shap Blue Qy O.S. Sheet (83) 565104 (M) 108

Shap Granite Qy O.S. Sheet (83) 554084 (M) 18

Shaw Fell O.S. Sheet (84) 692745 (M) 67

Shelve O.S. Sheet (137) 336990 (M) 6, 8, 27, 34, 42, 62

Sheppey O.S. Sheet (179) 020725 (M) 2, 68

Skiddaw O.S. Sheet (89) 260291 (M) 8, 10, 18, 34

Smalldale O.S. Sheet (119) 165815 (M) 6, 18, 34

Snailbeach O.S. Sheet (126) 375022 (M) 6, 8, 27, 34, 62

Southend O.S. Sheet (68) 691084 (M) 111, 113

Start Point O.S. Sheet (202) 830371 (M) 53, 64, 87, 116

Storr O.S. Sheet (24) 500540 (M) 15, 23, 42

Strath Glass O.S. Sheet (26) 370345 (M) 67

Strath Naver O.S. Sheet (10) 697613 (M) 108

Strathpeffer O.S. Sheet (26) 484582 (M) 108

Stromness O.S. Sheet (6) 253090 (M) 34

Strontian O.S. Sheet (40) 830659 (M) 6, 8, 34, 62, 100, 107

Strumble Head O.S. Sheet (157) 895414 (M) 106, 113

Suisgill O.S. Sheet (17) 901236 (M) 54, 71, 108

T

Talisker Bay O.S. Sheet (32) 314305 (M) 22, 100, 113

Tenby O.S. Sheet (158) 130005 (M) 111, 113

Tintagel O.S. Sheet (200) 060885 (M) 26

Tiree O.S. Sheet (46) (M) 52, 75, 87, 108

Tiroran O.S. Sheet (48) 479279 (M) 98

Treak Cliff O.S. Sheet (119) 135828 (M) 6, 18, 34

Tweed, R. O.S. Sheet (74) 825388 (M) 102, 111, 113

U

Usan O.S. Sheet (54) 726546 (M) 6, 24, 26, 42, 57, 68, 102, 111, 113, 114, 115

W

Walla Crag O.S. Sheet (89) 275215 (M) 26, 42, 78, 87, 102

Wanlockhead O.S. Sheet (71) 873129 (M) 6, 8, 18, 19, 26, 27, 34, 47, 49, 60, 62, 71, 73, 80, 81, 82, 106

Warden Point O.S. Sheet (178) 020725 (M) 2, 8, 76

Wast Water O.S. Sheet (89) 160060 (M) 108

Waterswallows Qy O.S. Sheet (119) 080751 (M) 6, 26, 10, 2, 111

Weydale Qy O.S. Sheet (12) 157653 (M) 99

Wheal Cock O.S. Sheet (203) 363338 (M) 18, 35, 54, 56, 74, 78, 102, 104, 108, 113

Wheal Gorland O.S. Sheet (203) 732428 (M) 24, 80, 82

Wheal Phoenix O.S. Sheet (186) 263723 (M) 35, 73, 80, 82, 92, 104

Whin Sill, Holy Island O.S. Sheet (75) 138417 (M) 26, 27, 42, 111

Whin Sill, Teesdale O.S. Sheet (92) 902268 (M) 26, 27, 42, 111

Whitby O.S. Sheet (94) 900110 (M) 6, 42, 76, 78, 111, 113

Wigtown Bay O.S. Sheet (83) 530520 (M) 102

Wiseman's Bridge O.S. Sheet (158) 145061 (M) 6, 26, 27

Wrekin, The O.S. Sheet (127) 626081 (M) 108

Y

Yate O.S. Sheet (172) 725830 (M) 9

BIBLIOGRAPHY AND FURTHER READING

Geology and Mineralogy

Ager, D. V. and Smith, W. E., Geologists Association Guide No. 2: *The Coast of South Devon and Dorset between Branscombe and Burton Bradstock*, 1973.

Bauer, M., *Precious Stones*, Vol. 2, Griffin, London, 1904.

Baur, J., *Minerals, Rocks and Precious Stones*, Octopus, London, 1974.

Bennison and Wright, *The Geological History of the British Isles*, Edward Arnold, London, 1969.

Borner, R. (translated and edited by W. Mykura), *Minerals, Rocks and Gemstones*, Oliver and Boyd, Edinburgh, 1967.

Calder, N., *Restless Earth*, B.B.C., London, 1972.

Chatwin, C. P., British Regional Geology *The Hampshire Basin and Adjoining Areas*, H.M.S.O., London, 1960.

Earp, J. R. and Hains, B. A., British Regional Geology *The Welsh Borderland*, H.M.S.O., London, 1971.

Edmonds, M. A. McKeown, M. C. and Williams, M., British Regional Geology *South West England*, H.M.S.O., London 1969.

Edwards, M. A. and Trotter, F. M., British Regional Geology *The Pennines and Adjacent Areas*, H.M.S.O., London, 1954.

Ellis, C., *The Pebbles on the Beach*, Faber and Faber, London, 1957.

Firsoff, V. Axel, *Gemstones of the British Isles*, Oliver and Boyd, Edinburgh, 1971.

Ford, T. D. and Sarjeant, W. A. S., *The Peak District Mineral Index*, Bulletin of Peak District Mines Historical Society 1963–5.

Freir, D. S., 'Minerals of the North Coast', *Gems*, 6 (5), 1974, p. 9.

Frondel, C., *The (Dana's) System of Mineralogy*, Vol. 3, Silica Minerals, Wiley, New York, 1962.

George, T. Neville, British Regional Geology *South Wales*, H.M.S.O., London, 1970.

Greg, R. P. and Lettsom, W. G., *Manual of the Mineralogy of Great Britain and Ireland*, John Van Voorst, London, 1858.

Greig, D. C., British Regional Geology *The South of Scotland,* H.M.S.O., Edinburgh, 1971.

Hains, B. A. and Horton, A., British Regional Geology *Central England,* H.M.S.O., London 1969.

Heddle, M. Forster (edited by J. G. Goodchild), *The Mineralogy of Scotland,* Vols. 1 & 2, David Douglas, Edinburgh, 1901.

Holmes, A., *Principles of Physical Geology,* Thomas Nelson & Sons, London, 1944.

Kellaway, G. A. and Welch, F. B. A., British Regional Geology *Bristol and Gloucester District,* H.M.S.O., London, 1948.

McCallien, W. J., *Scottish Gem Stones,* Quantum Reprints, London, 1967.

MacGregor, A. R., *Fife and Angus Geology,* Blackwood, Edinburgh, 1968.

Park and MacDiarmid, *Ore Deposits,* W. H. Freeman, 1975.

Phemister, J., British Regional Geology *Scotland: The Northern Highlands,* H.M.S.O., Edinburgh, 1960.

Read, H. H., British Regional Geology *The Grampian Mountains,* H.M.S.O., Edinburgh, 1948.

Richey, J. E., British Regional Geology *Scotland: The Tertiary Volcanic District,* H.M.S.O., Edinburgh, 1935.

Rodgers, P. R., *Agate Collecting in Britain,* B. T. Batsford Ltd., London, 1975.

Rodgers, P. R., 'Mineral Collecting in the Hebrides', *Gem Craft,* 2 (7), 1975, p. 445.

Rodgers, P. R., 'Scotland's Quartz Gemstones', *Gems,* 7 (5), 1975, p. 9.

Rodgers, P. R., 'The Derbyshire Marbles', *Gems* 4 (3), 1972, p. 2.

Rodgers, P. R., *Yorkshire Minerals,* Dalesman, Clapham, Yorks., 1975.

Rogers, C., *A Collector's Guide to Minerals, Rocks and Gemstones in Cornwall and Devon,* Bradford Barton, Truro, 1968.

Shackleton, E. H., *Lakeland Geology,* Dalesman, Clapham, Yorks., 1966.

Sherlock, R. L., British Regional Geology *London and Thames Valley,* H.M.S.O., London, 1960.

Smith, B. and George, T. Neville, British Regional Geology *North Wales,* H.M.S.O., London, 1961.

Stamp, L. Dudley, *Britain's Structure and Scenery,* Collins, London, 1946.

Taylor, B. J., Burgess, I. C., Land, D. H., Mills, D. A. C., Smith, D. B., and Warren, P. T., British Regional Geology *Northern England,* H.M.S.O., London, 1971.

Lapidary

Hutton, H., *Practical Gemstone Craft*, Viking, London, 1971.

Scarfe, H., *The Lapidary Manual*, B. T. Batsford, London, 1975.

Sinkanas, J., *Gem Cutting, A Lapidary Manual*, D. Van Nostrand, Princetown, New Jersey, 1962.

Sperisen, F. J., *The Art of Lapidary*, Bruce Publishing Co., Milwaukee, Wisconsin, 1961.

Victors, *Gem Tumbling and Baroque Jewellery Making*, Victor Agate Shop, California.

The following catalogue describes the identifiable characteristics of the minerals, these being listed under predominent colour, in order of increasing hardness. It is impossible to list all Britain's minerals within these pages, but only the rarer minerals have been omitted. Should you find a mineral which you are unable to identify then I would suggest that you take the specimen in question to a museum where the resident geologist may be able to help you. For further information regarding mineral localities see the Locality List.

MINERAL CATALOGUE

NO.	COLOUR	NAME	HARD-NESS	STREAK	LUSTRE	CRYSTAL FORM	FRACTURE
COLOURLESS–WHITE							
I	white, grey, greenish-yellow	TALC $Mg_3[(OH)_2Si_4O_{10}]$	1–1·5	white	greasy	monoclinic	uneven
2 ★	colourless, white, yellow, grey, red	GYPSUM $Ca(SO_4).2H_2O$	1·5–2	white	pearly	monoclinic	conchoidal
3	colourless, white, blue, orange	HALITE (Rock Salt) NaCl	2	white	vitreous	cubic	brittle
4	white, yellowish-grey	HYDROZINCITE $Zn[(OH)_3Co_3]_2$	2–2·5	white	dull	monoclinic	brittle
5	colourless, white, yellow, greenish-brown	IRON ALUM (Halotrichite) $FeAl_2(SO_4)_4.22H_2O$	2·5	white	silky	monoclinic	
6	colourless, white	CALCITE $CaCo_3$	3	white	vitreous	hexagonal	conchoidal
7	colourless, white, grey, violet	ANHYDRITE $Ca(So_4)$	3–3·5	white	vitreous	orthorhombic	brittle
8 ★	colourless, white, pink, yellow, red, blue	BARYTE $Ba(SO_4)$	3–3·5	white	vitreous	orthorhombic	brittle
9	colourless, white, yellowish, flesh-coloured	CELESTITE $Sr(SO_4)$	3–3·5	white	pearly	orthorhombic	brittle
10	white, yellow, grey	WITHERITE $BaCo^3$	3–3·5	white	vitreous	orthorhombic	brittle
11	white, grey, yellow, green	STRONTIANITE $SrCo_3$	3.5–4	white	vitreous-greasy	orthorhombic	brittle
12	white, grey, yellowish-brown	ANKERITE $CaFe(CO_3)_2$	3·5–4	white	vitreous	hexagonal	brittle
13	colourless, white, yellow, violet, grey, blue, green, brown	ARAGONITE $CaCo_3$	3·5–4	white	vitreous	orthorhombic	brittle
14	colourless, white, grey, yellow, brown	DOLOMITE $CaMg(Co_3)_2$	3·5–4	white	pearly	hexagonal	brittle

CLEAVAGE	TRANSPARENCY	SPECIFIC GRAVITY	COMMON FORM	OCCURRENCE	LOCALITIES
perfect	translucent to opaque	2·6–2·8	massive, lamellar crystals	alteration product of serpentine	Glen Clova Portsoy
perfect	transparent to translucent	2·4	needle-shaped crystals, granular, scaly	in salt deposits (evaporite)	Chellaston (alabaster-satin spar) Penarth (alabaster) Warden Point, Sheppey (selenite)
perfect cube	transparent to translucent	2·1–2·2	cubic crystals, fibrous, massive	in salt deposits (evaporite)	Cheshire
very good	opaque	3·2–3·8	crypto-crystalline, massive, encrustation	weathering product of zinc ores	in Pennine orefield
	translucent	1·8–2	acicular crystals, fibrous	weathering product of pyrite	common at locations which yield pyrite
perfect rhombohedral	transparent to opaque	2·6–2·8	rhombohedral, scalenohedral crystals, massive, stalactitic	common as crystals in rock cavities, and as stalactites and stalagmites	widespread particularly in limestone areas
good	transparent	3	compact, fibrous, lamellar	in salt deposits and hydrothermal veins	Mountfield
good	transparent to translucent	4·4	cockscomb, tabular needle-shaped crystals, reniform, massive	in ore veins, in fissures in sedimentary rocks	Arbor Low (oakstone) Dirtlow Rake Shelve Warden Point, Sheppey
perfect	transparent to translucent	4	massive, fibrous, granular	in veins in limestone and with gypsum and rock salt (evaporite)	Yate
good	transparent to translucent	4·2	columnar, tabular crystals, botryoidal, granular	common in lead ore veins with baryte	Skiddaw
distinct	transparent to translucent	3·7	needle-shaped crystals, fibrous, compact	in ore veins	Strontian
very good	opaque	3	rhombohedral, twinned crystals, granular, compact	in siderite deposits, in ore veins	Mill Close Mine
poor	transparent to opaque	2·9	massive, fibrous, radiating	with gypsum and iron ores; deposit from hot springs; sometimes in vesicals in volcanic rocks	Beckermet Mine
good	transparent to translucent	3	saddle-shaped crystals, granular, massive	formed by replacement of calcite; in ore veins; in gypsum beds	Masson Hill Millclose Mine Penberthy Crofts

NO.	COLOUR	NAME	HARD-NESS	STREAK	LUSTRE	CRYSTAL FORM	FRACTURE
15	colourless, white, yellow, grey	STILBITE $(CaNa_2)$-$[Al_2Si_6O_{16}].6H_2O$	3·5–4	white	pearly	monoclinic	uneven
16	white, yellow, green, blue, brown	WAVELLITE $Al_3[(OH)_3$-$(PO_4)_2].5H_2O$	3·5–4	white	silky	orthorhombic	brittle
17	white, yellow, greenish-grey	BARYTO-CALCITE $BaCa(Co_3)_2$	4	white	vitreous	monoclinic	brittle
18 ★	colourless, yellow, violet, green, blue, pink, red	FLUORITE (Fluorspar, Blue John) CaF_2	4	white	vitreous	cubic	conchoidal
19	colourless, white, bluish, greenish, yellowish, grey	HEMIMORPHITE $Zn_4[(OH)_2$-$Si_2O_7]H_2O$	4·5–5	white	pearly	orthorhombic	brittle
20	greenish-white, yellowish	SCHEELITE $Ca(WO_4)$	4·5–5	white	adamantine	tetragonal	uneven
21	white, grey	PECTOLITE $Ca_2NaH(Si_3O_9)$	5	white	silky	triclinic	brittle
22	colourless, white, yellowish, reddish	ANALCITE $Na(AlSi_2O_6).H_2O$	5–5·5	white	vitreous	cubic	conchoidal
23	colourless, white, yellowish, red, pink	NATROLITE $Na_2Al_2Si_3$-$O_{10}.2H_2O$	5–5·5	white	vitreous	orthorhombic	brittle
24	white, grey, yellow-brown	OPAL $SiO_2.nH_2O$	5·5–6·5	white	waxy	amorphous	conchoidal
25	white, red, yellowish	ALBITE $Na(AlSi_3O_8)$ FELDSPAR FAMILY	6	white	pearly	monoclinic	brittle
26 ★	colourless	ROCK CRYSTAL SiO_2 (QUARTZ FAMILY)	7	white	vitreous	hexagonal	conchoidal
27 ★	white, yellowish	MILKY QUARTZ SiO_2 (QUARTZ FAMILY)	7	white	vitreous	hexagonal	conchoidal
28	colourless, yellow-blue, green, red	TOPAZ $Al_2(F_2SiO_4)$	8	white	vitreous	orthorhombic	uneven
29	colourless, yellow-green, blue, red, grey, black	DIAMOND C	10	white	adamantine	cubic	conchoidal

CLEAVAGE	TRANSPARENCY	SPECIFIC GRAVITY	COMMON FORM	OCCURRENCE	LOCALITIES
perfect	transparent to translucent	2·2	tabular, lamellar, columnar, compact	in vesicals in volcanic rocks	Storr, Skye
good	translucent	2·4	globular, reniform, fibrous	in sandstone, some schists and quartzite	Hensbarrow Barnstable
very good	transparent to translucent	3·7	prismatic crystals, granular, massive	in ore veins with baryte	Alston moor
perfect	transparent to translucent	3·1	cubic crystals, granular, massive	in ore veins in igneous and sedimentary rocks	widespread, good locations include: Cligga Mine Smalldale Wanlockhead Castleton—Blue John
very good	transparent to translucent	3·4	tabular crystals, massive, reniform, mamillary	in veins in limestone, often associated with galena and sphalerite	Wanlockhead
brittle	translucent to opaque	6	crystalline, reniform, massive, encrustation	in pegmatites and mineral veins; contact zones of igneous rocks with lime-rich sedimentary rocks	Carrock Mine
good	translucent	2·8	fibrous, massive, reniform, long columnar crystals	in cracks and fissures in igneous rocks	Corstophine Hill Talisker Bay
poor	translucent to opaque	2·2	crystalline, massive granular, earthy	in cavities in basalt; in ore veins	Talisker Bay
very good	transparent to opaque	2·3	acicular, columnar crystals, fibrous, massive	in cavities in basalt and other igneous rocks	Burntisland Campsie Fells Scoor, Mull
none	translucent to opaque	2–2·3	veins, nodules, compact botryoidal. Not normally opalescent	in ore veins and vesicals in volcanic rock	Friden Glebe Mine Wheal Gorland
very good	translucent	2·6	tabular, columnar, acicular crystals, compact, granular	in pegmatites; in ore veins; in crystalline schists	Portsoy Tintagel
poor	transparent	2·6	crystalline	in cavities and fissures in igneous rocks; in ore veins	Calton Hill Quarry Miller's Dale Tintagel
poor	translucent to opaque	2·6	crystalline, massive	common in veins in many rocks, in ore veins	Cairngorm Dulcote Quarry The Cheviot
very good	transparent to translucent	3·5	columnar crystals, compact, massive	in pegmatites; in granites; in tin ore veins	Cairngorm Cligga Mine Goatfell
very good	transparent to opaque	3·5	octahedral, cubic crystals	in ultra basic rocks	3 miles N.E. of Ben Hope

NO.	COLOUR	NAME	HARD-NESS	STREAK	LUSTRE	CRYSTAL FORM	FRACTURE
GREY							
30	lead-grey	MOLYBDENITE MoS_2	1–1·5	grey-green	metallic	hexagonal	flexible
31	steel-grey	JAMESONITE $4PbS_1FeS.3Sb_2S_3$	2–2·5	grey-black	metallic	monoclinic	soft
32	lead-grey	STIBNITE Sb_2S_3	2–2·5	black-dark grey	metallic	orthorhombic	conchoidal
33	grey, grey-black	PYROLUSITE MnO_2	2–7 variable	black	metallic-indistinct	tetragonal	brittle
34	lead-grey, bluish	GALENA $Pb\ S$	2·5	grey-black	metallic	cubic	brittle-soft
35	grey-white, dark grey	CHALCOCITE Cu_2S	2·5–3	dark grey	metallic	orthorhombic	conchoidal
36	grey-black, silver, white	SILVER Ag	2·5–3	silver-white	metallic	cubic	malleable
37	grey, white, colourless, blackish	ANGLESITE $PbSo_4$	3	white	greasy	orthorhombic	conchoidal
38	grey, black, brown, yellow	LIMONITE $Fe_2O_3.nH_2O$	5–5·5	rusty brown	silky-greasy-dull	orthorhombic	conchoidal-fibrous
39	light grey, white, greenish	TREMOLITE $Ca_2Mg_8(OH,F)_2(Si_4O_{11})_2$	5–6	white	silky	monoclinic	brittle
40	grey, tin-white	ARSENOPYRITE $FeAsS$	5·5–6	black	metallic	orthorhombic	brittle
41	grey, white, green, brown	SILLIMANITE $Al_2(OSiO_4)$	6–7	white	vitreous-silky	orthorhombic	brittle
42 *	grey, blue-grey, yellow-grey	CHALCEDONY SiO_2 (QUARTZ FAMILY)	6·5–7	white	vitreous-silky	hexagonal	conchoidal
43	grey, reddish-brown	ANDALUSITE $Al_2(OSiO_4)$	7	white	vitreous-dull	orthorhombic	uneven
BLACK							
44	black, steel-grey	GRAPHITE C	1–2	black-grey	dull	hexagonal	flexible
45	black, dark brown	WAD $MnO_2.nH_2O$	1·5	black, dark-brown	dull	amorphous	rough

LEAVAGE	TRANSPARENCY	SPECIFIC GRAVITY	COMMON FORM	OCCURRENCE	LOCALITIES
erfect	opaque	4·6–4·7	flat, tabular crystals, massive, compact	in tin ore deposits, and quartz veins	found in tin ore deposits in Cornwall shap
ear	opaque	5·7	long, acicular crystals, compact, massive, feather-like	in ore veins	Leadhills
erfect	opaque	4·6	columnar crystals, fibrous, granular, massive	in ore veins	The Knipe
ood	opaque	5	earthy, reniform, massive, needle-shaped crystals	in ore veins; sedimentary deposits	Croscombe East Harp Tree
erfect	opaque	7·2–7·6	cubic-octahedral, crystals, compact, massive, granular	in ore veins	widespread in Pennines other localities include Leadhills Combe Martin
distinct	opaque	5·7	columnar, needle-shaped crystals, massive, granular, earthy	in ore veins, with other copper minerals	Habberley Wheal Phoenix
ckly	opaque	10·5	compact	in ore veins; rare in an uncombined form in Britain	Coombe Martin Minerva
ood	transparent to translucent	6·4	short, prismatic, columnar crystals; compact, granular earthy	in oxidation zone of lead ore deposits	Pary's Copper Mine
ne	opaque	3·6	earthy, fibrous oolitic, stalactitic, concretionary	weathering product of iron deposits; sedimentary deposits in ore veins	Botallack Mine
ry good	translucent	3	fibrous, radial, compact, asbestos-like	in metamorphic limestone and dolomite	The Lizard
ar	opaque	6·2–6·8	tubular crystals, compact, fibrous, granular	in ore veins	Kit Hill
ry good	translucent	3·2	columnar crystals; fibrous, radial, compact	in crystalline schists; in contact metamorphic rocks	Glen Clova
ne	translucent	2·5–2·6	crypto-crystalline, reniform, botryoidal, stalactitic, nodules, concretions	in fissures and cavities in basic volcanic rocks; in ore veins	Lyme Regis Melsetter Montrose
od-istinct	transparent to opaque	3·2	columnar crystals, granular, compact, fibrous	in metamorphic rocks; in schists and pegmatites	Cligga Mine Meldon Quarry
fect	opaque	2·1	massive, earthy, dendritic	in limestone; in metamorphic rocks and pegmatites	New Cumnock
ne	opaque	2–4 variable	earthy, sooty, dendritic, botryoidal	in sedimentary rocks as nodules; in volcanic rocks; in oxidised zone of manganese ores	Normans Law The Cheviot Wadbury (Mendip Hills)

NO.	COLOUR	NAME	HARD-NESS	STREAK	LUSTRE	CRYSTAL FORM	FRACTUR
46	black, dark brown	BIOTITE $k(Mg,Fe,Mn)_3$ $[(OH,F)_2AlSi_3O_{10}]$ (IRON MICA)	2·5–3	white-grey	vitreous-pearly	monoclinic	flexible
47	black, brown, red, iridescent tarnish on weathering	BORNITE Cu_5FeS_4	3	black	metallic	cubic	brittle, conchoidal
48	black, grey	TETRA-HEDRITE $(Cu,Zn,Ag,Fe)^3$ $(Sb,As)S_{3-4}$	3–4	black	metallic	cubic	sub-conchoidal, uneven
49	black, brown, yellowish	GOETHITE $a-FeOOH$	5–5·5	brown, brownish-yellow	silky-dull	orthorhombic	rough
50	black, brownish, greenish	HORNBLENDE (complex silicate)	5–6	grey, brownish-green	vitreous	monoclinic	uneven
51	black, dark brown	WOLFRAMITE $(Mn,Fe)WO_4$	5–5·5	black-brown	metallic greasy	monoclinic	uneven, bri
52	black, greenish-black	AUGITE $(Ca,Mg,Fe_2,-$ $Fe_3,Ti,Al)_2$ $[(Si,Al)_2O_6]$	5·5	greyish-green	vitreous	monoclinic	conchoidal
53	black	ILMENITE $FeTiO_3$	5·5	black, brown	sub-metallic, dull	hexagonal	conchoidal
54	black	MAGNETITE Fe_3O_4	5·5	black	metallic, dull, greasy	cubic	conchoidal brittle
55	black, steel-grey, tarnishes	SPECULARITE Fe_2O_3 (IRON GLANCE)	6	cherry-red, brown	metallic, dull	hexagonal	uneven, brittle
56	black, brown	CASSITERITE SnO_2	6·5	white-pale yellow	adamantine, metallic	tetragonal	conchoidal brittle
57 *	black, deep brown	MORION SiO_2 (QUARTZ FAMILY)	7	white	vitreous	hexagonal	conchoidal
58	black	SCHORL $NaMg_3Al_6$ $[(OH)_{1+3}(BO_3)_{3-}$ $Si_6O_{18}]$ (Black Tourmaline)	7–7·5	white	vitreous-greasy	hexagonal	conchoida uneven, brittle
BROWN							
59	brown, grey, colourless, yellow, green	MUSCOVITE $KAL_2[(OH,-$ $F)_2AlSi_3O_{10}]$ (MICA FAMILY)	2–2·5	white	pearly-vitreous	monoclinic	flexible
60	brown, grey, yellowish-white	CERUSSITE $PbCO_3$	3–3·5	white	adamantine-greasy	orthorhombic	conchoida

CLEAVAGE	TRANSPARENCY	SPECIFIC GRAVITY	COMMON FORM	OCCURRENCE	LOCALITIES
perfect	transparent to translucent	3	compact, lamellar, scaly, tabular crystals	in granites, pegmatites; in metamorphic rocks	Glen Elg Milton Portsoy
none	opaque	4·9–5·3	granular, massive, coatings, cube-shaped crystals	in copper ore veins	Carrock Ecton Hill
none	opaque	4·4–5	compact, granular, massive	in hydrothermal ore veins	Coombe Martin St Just
good	translucent to opaque	3·8–4·3	massive, powdery, radiating fibrous aggregates	in sedimentary rocks; in oxidised zone of ore veins	Botallack Mine Dulcote Quarry
perfect	opaque	2·9–3·4	fibrous, granular, massive crystalline	in metamorphic rocks	Balta Sound
very good	opaque	7·1–7·5	massive, radiating aggregates, needles	in hydrothermal ore veins near granite; often associated with tin ores	Carrock Cligga Mine
good	translucent to opaque	3·4	massive, granular, fibrous, crystalline	in metamorphic and basic igneous rocks	The Cuillins Tiree
one	translucent to opaque	4·5–5	granular, platy, radiating scales, crystalline	in basic igneous rocks	Start Point
imperfect	opaque	5·2	compact, massive, granular, crystalline	in schists; in basalts	Wheal Cock
one	opaque	5·2–5·3	crystalline	in hydrothermal ore veins	Beckermet Mine Egremont
distinct	opaque	6·8–7·1	massive, fibrous, crystalline	associated with granites and pegmatites	Wheal Cock
one	transparent to translucent	2·6	short, columnar, hexagonal crystals (pyramids)	in cavities in intrusive and extrusive igneous rocks	Cairngorm Calton Hill Quarry Cheviot Hills
one	opaque	3–3·1	massive, compact, long columnar crystals	in granites and pegmatites; in metamorphic limestone and schist	Carn Brea Mines Roche Rocks
perfect	transparent to translucent	2·8	scaly, massive, thin columnar crystals	common in metamorphic and some igneous rocks	Portsoy Strath Naver
distinct	transparent to translucent	6·5	massive, reniform, compact, columnar tabular crystals	in weathering zone of lead ores	Leadhills Wanlockhead

NO.	COLOUR	NAME	HARD-NESS	STREAK	LUSTRE	CRYSTAL FORM	FRACTURE
61	brown, yellowish, green, grey	SIDERITE $FeCO_3$	3·5–4	white-yellowish	vitreous-pearly	hexagonal	brittle
62	brown, grey, black, red, yellow	SPHALERITE ZnS (ZINC BLENDE)	3·5–4	white-yellow-brown	adamantine-greasy	cubic	brittle
63	brown, bronze, grey, green	BRONZITE $(Mg,Fe)_2$ $[Si_2O_6]$	5–6	white-grey	metallic-silky	orthorhombic	none
64	brown, yellow, red	RUTILE TiO_2	6·5	white	adamantine	tetragonal	brittle
65	brown, grey, violet, green	AXINITE $Ca_2(Fe,Mn)Al_2$ $[BO_3OH.-Si_4O_{12}]$	6·5–7	white	vitreous	triclinic	conchoidal-brittle
66	brown, greenish-black, olive-green	OLIVINE $(Mg,Fe)_2$ $[SiO_4]$	6·5–7	white	vitreous-greasy	orthorhombic	conchoidal
67	brown, red, green, yellow, blue, orange, colourless	ZIRCON $Zr[SiO_4]$	6·5–7·5	white	vitreous-adamantine-greasy	tetragonal	conchoidal
68 ★	brown, smoky	SMOKY QUARTZ SiO_2 (QUARTZ FAMILY)	7	white	vitreous	hexagonal	conchoidal
69	brown, black	STAUROLITE $Al_4[Fe(OH)_2-O_2(SiO_4)_2]$	7–7·5	grey-white	vitreous-dull	orthorhombic	conchoidal-uneven
YELLOW							
70 ★	wax-yellow, honey	AMBER $C_{12}H_{20}O$	2–2·5	white	resinous	amorphous	conchoidal
71	gold	GOLD Au	2·5–3	gold	metallic	cubic	ductile
72	yellow, orange, brown	GREENOCKITE CdS	3–3·5	yellow	adamantine	hexagonal	brittle
73	brass-yellow	CHALCO-PYRITE $CuFeS_2$	3·5–4	greenish-black	metallic	tetragonal	brittle
	yellow, greenish-white	APATITE $Ca_5(F[PO_4]_3)$	5	white	vitreous	hexagonal	conchoidal
75	yellow, brown, white	SPHENE $CaTi(OSiO_4)$	5–5·5	white	vitreous	monoclinic	conchoidal
76	gold, brass-yellow	PYRITE FeS_2	6–6·5	greenish-black	metallic	cubic	conchoidal

CLEAVAGE	TRANSPARENCY	SPECIFIC GRAVITY	COMMON FORM	OCCURRENCE	LOCALITIES
perfect rhombohedral	translucent to opaque	3·8	massive, granular, oolitic	in sediments as nodules; in metasomatic ore veins	Cleveland
very good	transparent to opaque	3·9–4·2	radiating, fibrous, aggregates; crystalline	in ore veins	Shelve Wanlockhead Wheal Mary Ann
good (variable)	translucent to opaque	3·2–3·5	fibrous, granular, crystals rare	in basic rocks	The Lizard
good	transparent to translucent	4·2–4·3	acicular crystals, granular, compact, rarely as inclusions in quartz	with quartz in igneous and metamorphic rocks	Start Point
good	transparent to translucent	3·3	tabular, wedge-shaped crystals, granular, compact	in metamorphic rocks and ore deposits	Meldon Quarry
good	transparent to translucent	3·3	tabular crystals, granular, massive	in basic igneous rocks	Calton Hill Quarry The Lizard
imperfect	transparent to translucent	3·9–4·8	columnar, needle-shaped crystals, granular	in igneous rocks and crystalline schists	Ben Hope Elie Ness Ennerdale
none	transparent	2·6	crystals	in vesicals in volcanic rocks and in pegmatites	Cairngorm Calton Hill Quarry
good	translucent to opaque	3·7–3·8	columnar crystals (cross-shaped twins)	in metamorphic rocks	The Lizard
brittle	transparent to translucent	1–1·1	pebbles	on East Coast beaches	Aldeburgh Bridlington Guardbridge
none	opaque	14·5–19·3	grains	in association with intrusive igneous rocks	Cligga Mine Kildonan
good	translucent	4·9–5	short columnar crystals, earthy	in weathering zone of zinc deposits	Bishopstown
indistinct	opaque	4·1–4·3	crystals, reniform, granular, massive	common in ore deposits	Ecton Hill Pary's Copper Mine Wanlockhead
poor	translucent to opaque	3·2	crystals, granular, massive	in pegmatites	Carrock Mine Wheal Cock
good	transparent to translucent	3·5	crystals, granular	in igneous and metamorphic rocks	Culloden Ennerdale Llandrindod
indistinct	opaque	4·8–5	crystals, nodular, massive	in sulphide ore deposits	Ballachulish (in slate) Mill Close Mine Whitby

NO.	COLOUR	NAME	HARD-NESS	STREAK	LUSTRE	CRYSTAL FORM	FRACTURE
77	brass-yellow, greenish	MARCASITE FeS_2	6–6·5	greenish-black	metallic	orthorhombic	brittle
78 ★	yellow, orange	CARNELIAN SiO_2 (QUARTZ FAMILY)	6·5–7	white	vitreous-silky	hexagonal	conchoidal
79	lemon, yellow	CITRINE SiO_2 (QUARTZ FAMILY)	7	white	vitreous	hexagonal	conchoidal
GREEN							
80	green, bluish	CHRYSOCOLLA Cu_4H_4 $[(OH)_8-$ $Si_4O_{10}]$	2–4	pale green, bluish	greasy	monoclinic	conchoidal
81	green, yellow, brown	PYROMOR-PHITE $Pb_5[Cl.(PO_4)_3]$	3·5–4	white, yellowish	adamantine	hexagonal	uneven
82	emerald-green, dark green	MALACHITE $Cu_2[(OH)_2$ $CO_3]$	4	light green	vitreous	monoclinic	fibrous
83	green, yellow, white	SMITHSONITE $ZnCO_3$ (CALAMINE)	5	white	vitreous	hexagonal	brittle
84	dark green, pale green, white	ACTINOLITE $Ca_2(FeMg)_5$ $[Si_8O_{22}]$ $(OH)_2$	5–6	white	vitreous	monoclinic	brittle
85	green, bluish green	AMAZONITE $K[AlSi_3O_8]$ (FELDSPAR)	6	white	vitreous	hexagonal	uneven
86	green, greenish-white	PREHNITE $Ca_2Al[(OH)_2$ $AlSi_3O_{10}]$	6–6·5	white	vitreous-pearly	orthorhombic	uneven
87	dark green, grey, black, brown	EPIDOTE $Ca_2(Fe,Al) Al_2$ $[OOHSiO_4-$	6–7	white-grey	vitreous	monoclinic	conchoidal
88	green, brownish yellow	IDOCRASE $Ca_{10}(Mg, Fe)_2-$ $Al_4[(OH_4)l$ $(SiO_4)_5l$ $(Si_2O_7)_2]$	6·5	white	vitreous	tetragonal	brittle
89	green, whitish, yellowish	JADEITE $NaAl[Si_2O_6]$	6·5–7	white	vitreous-greasy	monoclinic	uneven
90	green, bluish	CORDIERITE $Mg_2[Al_4-$ $Si_5O_{18}]$	7–7·5	white	vitreous-greasy	orthorhombic	conchoidal
91	yellowish-green, bluish-green, dark green, red	BERYL Al_2Be_3 $[Si_6O_{18}]$	7·5–8	white	vitreous-dull	hexagonal	conchoidal

CLEAVAGE	TRANSPARENCY	SPECIFIC GRAVITY	COMMON FORM	OCCURRENCE	LOCALITIES
indistinct	opaque	4·8–4·9	crystals, nodular, massive	in ore deposits, clays and chalk	Coombe Martin Folkestone
none	translucent	2·5–2·6	crypto-crystalline, botry-oidal, nodules	in cavities in volcanic rocks; with flint	Colchester Carnelian Bay Normans Law
poor	transparent	2·6	crystalline	in cavities in igneous rocks	Carrock Mine Marazion
none	translucent to opaque	2–2·3	botryoidal, massive	in oxidation zone of copper ore deposits	Carrock Wanlockhead Wheal Phoenix
none	translucent	6·7–7	crystals, encrustations	in weathering zone of lead ore deposits	Wanlockhead
good	translucent to opaque	4	encrustation, massive, botryoidal	in weathering zone of copper ores	Alderley Edge Ecton Hill Wanlockhead
very good	translucent	4·3–4·5	encrustation, crystals, botryoidal	weathering product of zinc ores	common in Pennines Rowbarrow
good	opaque	2·9–3·1	parallel fibrous aggregates	in basic igneous rocks which have undergone meta-morphism	Ramsley
very good	translucent	2·5	massive, tabular crystals	in igneous rocks and pegmatites	Ben Loyal
clear	transparent to trans-lucent	2·8–3	reniform, tabular columnar crystals	in cavities in basic igneous rocks, and in crystalline schists	Barrhead Hartfield Moss
very good	translucent	3·3–3·5	columnar crystals, massive	in fissures in basic volcanic rocks	Goatfell The Lizard Walla Crag
none	transparent to trans-lucent	3·4	crystals, massive	in metamorphic limestones	Portsoy
none	translucent	3·2–3·3	crystals, massive	in crystalline schists	The Lizard
good	transparent to trans-lucent	2·6	platy crystals	in pegmatites in metamorphic rocks	The Lizard
indistinct	transparent to trans-lucent	2·6	columnar crystals, compact, fibrous	in granites and granite pegmatites	Cairngorm Mountains St Day

NO.	COLOUR	NAME	HARD-NESS	STREAK	LUSTRE	CRYSTAL FORM	FRACTURE
BLUE							
92	azure-blue, blackish-blue	AZURITE $Cu_3[OHCO_3]_2$	3·5	blue	vitreous-dull	monoclinic	brittle-uneven
93	sky-blue, greenish	TURQUOISE $CuAl_6[(OH)_2PO_4]_4$	5–6	white	greasy	triclinic	conchoidal-brittle
94	blue, grey, white, greenish	KYANITE $Al_2[OSiO_4]$	4·5–7	white	vitreous-pearly	triclinic	brittle
95	blue, bluish-black	GLAUCOPHANE $Na_{2-3}MgFe_3.. Al_2[Si_8O_{22}] (OH)_{1-2}$	6–6·5	blue-grey	vitreous	monoclinic	rough
96	pale blue, pale green	BERYL Var- AQUAMARINE $Al_2Be_3 [Si_6O_{18}]$	7·5–8	white	vitreous	hexagonal	brittle
97	blue, black, red, brown	SPINEL $MgAl_2O_4$	8	white	vitreous	cubic	conchoidal
98	blue	SAPPHIRE Al_2O_3	9	white	vitreous	hexagonal	conchoidal-brittle
VIOLET							
99	violet, indigo, blue, black	VIVIANITE $Fe_3[PO_4]_2 8H_2O$	1·5–2	white	vitreous	monoclinic	into thin flexible plates
100	violet, reddish, greenish, white	APOPHYLITE $KCa_4[F(Si_4 O_{10})_2]8H_2O$	4–5	white	vitreous-pearly	tetragonal	brittle-uneven
101	violet, white, green, yellow, colourless, grey	SPODUMENE $LiAl(Si_2O_6)$	6·5–7	white	vitreous	monoclinic	brittle
102 ★	violet	AMETHYST SiO_2 (QUARTZ FAMILY)	7	white	vitreous-greasy	hexagonal	brittle-conchoidal
RED							
103	red, grey	CINNABAR HgS	2–2·5	red	adamantine-dull	hexagonal	uneven
104	copper-red, black-brown	COPPER	2.5–3	copper-red	metallic	cubic	ductile
105	red, reddish-brown	RHODONITE $CaMn_4 (Si_5O_{15})$	5·5–6·5	white	vitreous-pearly	triclinic	uneven
106 ★	red, brown, grey, black	HAEMATITE Fe_2O_3	5·5–5·6	red, reddish-brown	metallic-dull	hexagonal	uneven-fibrous
107	red, reddish-brown, grey-white	ORTHOCLASE $k[AlSi_3O_8]$ (FELDSPAR FAMILY)	6–6·5	white	vitreous-pearly	monoclinic	uneven-brittle

CLEAVAGE	TRANSPARENCY	SPECIFIC GRAVITY	COMMON FORM	OCCURRENCE	LOCALITIES
good	translucent to opaque	2·6	crystals, botryoidal, encrustation	in oxidation zones of copper ore deposits	Alderley Edge Ecton Hill Wheal Phoenix
none	opaque	2·6–2·9	crypto-crystalline, massive, botryoidal, veins & coatings	common in zone of weathering in aluminium-rich rocks	Hensbarrow
very good	transparent to translucent	3·6–3·7	lamellar; flat tabular crystals; radiating masses	in crystalline schists	Hillwick The Lizard
perfect	translucent	3–3·1	fibrous, massive	in metamorphic rocks	Anglesey
none	transparent	2·7	short columnar crystals	in pegmatites in granites and schists	Goatfell
very poor	transparent to translucent	3·5–4·1	small individual crystals	in igneous rocks and in contact zone of metamorphosed rocks	Glen Elg The Cuillins
none	transparent to opaque	4	small plates	in metamorphosed rocks	Carsaig Glebe Hill
very good	translucent to opaque	2·7	earthy, massive	replacement mineral in fossils (fish)	Achanarras Quarry Castletown
very good	transparent to translucent	2·3–2·4	pyramidal crystals, granular, massive	in cavities in basalt; in ore veins	Strontian Talisker Bay
very good	transparent to translucent	3·2	tubular, columnar, tabular	in pegmatites	Cairngorm Mountains
poor	transparent to translucent	2·6	hexagonal columnar crystals	in cavities in volcanic rocks	Dulcote Quarry Dunrobbin Glen Waterswallows Quarry
good	transparent to opaque	8·1	short columnar crystals, massive, encrustation	in mineral veins	Magpie Mine Masson Hill
none	opaque	8·5–9	tabular, crystals, dendritic encrustations	in ore veins; in basalt	Cligga Mine Wheal Phoenix
good	translucent	3·5	needle-shaped crystals, massive	in manganese ore deposits	Leadhills Meldon Quarry
none	opaque	5·2–5·3	rhombohedral crystals, compact, massive, mammillary	in hydrothermal ore veins	Criffel Egremont Leadhills
very good	transparent to translucent	2·5	columnar crystals, massive	in pegmatites in granite, schist and ore veins	Ben Hope Strontian

NO.	COLOUR	NAME	HARD-NESS	STREAK	LUSTRE	CRYSTAL FORM	FRACTURE
108	red	GARNET Grossular $Ca_3Al_2[SiO_4]_3$	7	white	glassy-fatty	cubic	brittle
	brown	Andradite $Ca_3Fe_2[SiO_4]_3$	6·5–7·5				
	blood-red	Pyrope $Mg_3Al_2[SiO_4]_3$	7–7·5				
	deep red	Almandine $Fe_3Al_2[SiO_4]_3$	7				
	brownish-red	Spessartite $Mn_3Al_2[SiO_4]_3$	7–7·5				
	emerald-green	Uvarovite $Ca_3Cr_2[SiO_4]_3$	7·5				
109	rose-red	ROSE QUARTZ SiO_2 (QUARTZ FAMILY)	7	white	greasy	hexagonal	conchoidal-brittle

MULTI-COLOURED

NO.	COLOUR	NAME	HARD-NESS	STREAK	LUSTRE	CRYSTAL FORM	FRACTURE
110 ★	green, yellow black, red, brown, mottled	SERPENTINE $Mg_6(OH)_8[Si_4O_{10}]$ (MINERAL SERPENTINE)	3–4	white	greasy-dull	monoclinic	conchoidal
111 ★	banded: grey, blue, pink, red, orange, yellow, green	AGATE SiO_2 (QUARTZ FAMILY)	7	white	vitreous-greasy-dull	none crypto-crystalline	conchoidal
112 ★	green with red spots	BLOODSTONE SiO_2 (QUARTZ FAMILY)	7	white	dull	none crypto-crystalline	rough
113 ★	red, yellow, green brown, mottled	JASPER SiO_2 (QUARTZ FAMILY)	7	white	greasy-dull	none crypto-crystalline	rough-conchoidal
114 ★	black-blue and white	ONYX	7	white	vitreous-greasy-dull	none crypto-crystalline	conchoidal
115 ★	red and white	SARD ONYX SiO_2 (QUARTZ FAMILY)					
116	green-pink (in one crystal)	TOURMALINE $NaFe_3Al_6[(OH)_4(BO_3)_3Si_6O_{18}]$	7–7·5	white	vitreous	hexagonal	uneven-brittle
117	red, blue, black, green, brown, grey	CORUNDUM Al_2O_3 (FOR SAPPHIRE SEE 98)	9	white	vitreous	hexagonal	brittle-conchoidal

CLEAVAGE	TRANSPARENCY	SPECIFIC GRAVITY	COMMON FORM		LOCALITIES
poor	transparent to opaque	3·4–4·6	crystals, grains	common in meta-morphic rocks (schists)	common throughout Scottish High-lands Elie Ness—pyrope Strathpeffer, Achnasheen The Lizard—almandine. Baltasound—uvarovite
none	translucent	2·6	crystals, massive	in pegmatites in granites, and volcanic rocks	Calton Hill Quarry Dulcote Quarry
none	translucent to opaque	2·5–2·6	micro, crystalline massive	in veins in serpentine rock	The Lizard
none	translucent to opaque	2·5–2·6	nodules, pebbles	in gas cavities in volcanic rocks	widespread in Central Scotland, and as pebbles on beaches throughout England
none	opaque	2·5–2·6	nodules, pebbles	in gas cavities in volcanic rocks	Bloodstone Hill
none	opaque	2·5–2·6	granular, massive, nodules, pebbles	in cracks and fissures in many types of rocks	widespread: to be found on most of Britain's beaches
none	translucent to opaque	2·5–2·6	nodules, (straight parallel bands)	in gas cavities in volcanic rocks	Colbost—sard onyx Dunure—onyx Lunan Bay—onyx, sard onyx Usan—onyx, sard onyx
none	transparent to trans-lucent	3–3·1	triangular columnar crystals	in pegmatites in granites and meta-morphic rocks	Aplite Quarry The Cheviot
none	transparent to opaque	3·9–4.1	barrel-shaped crystals, massive	in contact meta-morphosed rocks	Carrock Mine

INDEX